Still A Mess

By Allie West

Still A Mess by Allie West

Books may be purchased by contacting the publisher and author at: www.alliewest.com or info@alliewest.com

Editor: Attiyya Atkins, A+ Editing & Content Creation

Book Cover: Creative Companions

ISBN: 978-1-7364809-3-9

Printed in USA

About Allie West

Allie West's first novel, *A Dressed Up Mess* drew international acclaim, landing Allie on radio broadcasts and podcasts across the United States, Germany, United Kingdom, India and Nigeria. Fans praised her high energy, transparency, raw writing skills, and her unfiltered approach to life.

When she's not writing, this Tulsa, Oklahoma native works on building her *Messologist* brand. She speaks on the virtues of turning one's mess into their masterpiece by learning to master peace in their lives. Among the things she has a love for, Allie finds happiness in travel, music, dancing, food and everything fashion.□

She currently lives in Germany with her husband, where she uses her time positively to impact the lives of others.

Connect with Allie West via her website□www.alliewest.com

DEDICATION

This book is dedicated to my mother Dora L. Hunt who imported her gift of fashion and sense of style into my veins. Fashion runs through me like blood; if not for it, this this book would not exist. While writing this book, I realized that I am more like her than I ever knew, and the love that I thought I was missing from her was given to me in the form of style, grace, class and the ability to give zero $%&&$ while serving face. She gave me it to me in her language, not mine. At 81, she still brings it: makeup, hair, nails and clothes still on point and yes, she's *still a mess*!

To my young adult children Pookas and Chi-Chi (their childhood nicknames). I can only imagine what having me as a mother during the time I wrote this book must have been like. I was so engulfed in my own MESS that I didn't give you everything you needed. I am certain you both questioned God a time or two. Through it all, you two have learned to love and accept me and all of my mess. You guys are amazing human beings, and I am proud God allowed me to be your mom. You have watched me go from a mess to a masterpiece.

Family, friends and fans, I love and appreciate each and every one of you individually and collectively. I am grateful for your support and thank you for taking this journey with me.

-Allie West

Preface

No matter how naked I get, clothes will always cover me. I dream about them and envision styles that have not been created yet in my head. I love the feel of fabric, especially the softness of silk. I love the way a Lycra spandex blend snatches my waist, hoists my breast an accentuates my hourglass silhouette. The colors, textures, and prints lure me in. I don't leave the house unless I am flawless. I hear the clothes call out to me when I pass them on the racks. How can I leave them when they beg me to take them with me? Finding a great deal is euphoric, almost orgasmic...

Excerpt:

She dresses me nice, her claim to fame. If nothing else, my mother gifted me with a sense of style and a love for fashion. If there was a lack in love, affection, guidance, direction, it is compensated by designer clothes, purses and accessories. The Shopping Channel is the primary program on TV. Orders come to the house daily.

Everything that you can imagine is delivered to our house. We are in and out of countless stores: Dillard's, JC Penny, Trippets, NBC, Shoe Warehouse. We frequent every mall in Tulsa, Southland, South Roads Malls, even the nostalgic Northland, as well as Utica Square and Woodlands Hills—and if you know, don't too many black folks go to those two. If it isn't the mall, it's the Shopping Channel, and long before that were the boosters AKA shoplifters that my mother had on speed dial.

Everyone knew that when one or both of the twins pulled up alone or with their entourage of flunkies, unloading large garbage bags from the trunks and their backseat—it's on! They're so many bags that it reminds me of freshly raked leaves sitting in a row on the curb on a fall day. They talk really fast, almost like auctioneers and everything they pull out of the bags is "SHAAARRP!" they say.

"Oh, Darling, that was made just for you." "Come here, turn around, walk over there," shouting out commands like a drill sergeant.

"You see that? Now that's goooorrrgeous! Girl, that's bad—ain't that bad?"

They ask anyone within earshot so that they can co-sign, as to further convince Momma to purchase their stolen goods. The twins CUSS and are so proud of their accomplishments. They are always full of stories of how they outsmarted the salesperson in the store. "That bitch thought she had us, but we had something for her ass.... Didn't we chile?" The other chiming in "Sho did. I swear 'foe God that bitch thought she had us." I like listening to their entertaining stories just as much as I like trying on the clothes. To be their client is like being royalty, especially if they bring items just for you, delivered straight to your house. You're a BIG spender, money in the bag.

So, you know my mom is an A-Lister. I try on outfit after outfit: dresses, suits, pants, leather coats. You name it, they have it. Mom drops hundreds at a time to keep all of us looking fabulous. Heck, she even has an account with them. Dad's check comes every Monday, and they are there like the door-to-door insurance salesman to collect, and of course with more trash bags full of clothes.

So, this is how my addiction to shopping was born. Funny thing is I didn't realize it until now. Clothes are my coverup from anything that hurts. They are my escape from emptiness, loneliness and low self-esteem.

I dress it up, whatever the lack was as a child... Guess, Formalaries, Coach Bags, Fashion Fair makeup, Escape and other expensive perfumes dressed it up. Now the brand names have changed: Ann Taylor, Tahari, Calvin Klein, Jessica Simpson, Kate Spade, BCBG, INC International, Rachel Roy, Tina Turk, Gucci, M.A.C., and countless others, but the impact is the same.

My closet runneth over and my bank account runneth under. This is what shopping addiction looks like. I am no different than the addicts I thought I was nothing like.

Table of Contents

Happy New Year

The sunlight peering through the curtain introduces me to the New Year. I reach for Danny but he's already out of bed. He probably let Maxwell out for his morning routine. I stretch, take a deep breath, and exhale slowly. A smile spreads over my face as images of last night's love-making marathon flashes across my mind. *Ooh-Wee, that man knows he's gifted. Is it possible to be ad-dick-ted or dick-ma-tized? I think I am.* I laugh out loud. If I could bottle up his skills and sell them, I'd be rich. Life is good right now; I am in a decent head space. Perhaps I can make Tulsa work. I have a sense of peace that I have not felt in a long time. Wow, this year is gonna be monumental! There are so many milestones to celebrate: I turn forty, Daddy turns seventy, I graduate with my master's and my baby girl Cicely graduates from high school. Yes! Look out 2011—I am ready to take you by storm.

Danny interrupts my thoughts as he enters the room with fresh fruit, water and juice. He feeds me strawberries and grapes. I sip water and then the orange and cranberry juice mix. "Do you want to go to breakfast?" he asks.

"Sure," I say.

"You were magnificent last night," His Adam's apple dips when his deep voice moves.

"You were alright," I joke.

"Oh, really only alright?"

"Yeah, alright." He knows I am lying by the huge grin on my face.

"Well, I'll have to work on making sure I get better, Allison," he giggles.

We finish the fruit. The look in his eyes tells me he's ready to get to work. I shift the conversation.

"I'd better go shower." I kiss Danny on the cheek and head to the bathroom.

I step out of the shower refreshed, wrap a towel around me and open the bathroom door. Maxwell jumps on me and follows me to Danny's bedroom. He's a huge puppy, over seventy pounds and just two years old. He loves me, or at least the attention I give him. I think Maxwell is a bit jealous of Danny and vice versa.

"Go." Danny points to the door and sternly instructs Maxwell to leave. Maxwell walks out reluctantly, stops just outside the door, turns around and stares with his sad eyes. I laugh at him; and say to Danny "Leave him alone." He replies, "There is only one alpha male in this house and it ain't Maxwell. He knows who the boss is."

Sitting atop the bed, I rub the towel against my long hair.

"Will you lotion my back?" Danny picks up the lotion from the dresser and walks over to the bed.

He sits down behind me. I hear Danny snap the bottle open, then squeeze of the lotion and the rub of his palms rustling together. He strokes the nape of my neck and slowly works his way to my shoulders, then down to the small of my back. He reaches for more lotion, then works his way back up to my shoulders; this time he deeply massages them. I relax, his touch feels good. He plants soft kisses down my neck. I quietly moan. I feel the erectness of my nipples and the moisture between my legs.

"Lay down," Danny whispers in my ear. I immediately oblige. I lay on my stomach as he straddles me, his erect penis between by butt cheeks and back. He rubs my neck and gradually works his way down, applying just the right amount of pressure. I let out small sighs of relief as his hands glide down my body. He adjusts, his palms grasp my butt and eases in between my legs. I quiver. He teases me, gently taps his fingers along the lining of my vagina and lightly grabs the inside of my thighs. My legs shake, it's hard to resist his touch. He kisses the back of my knees and it tickles. I laugh. "What's the matter?" he slyly asks. "Oh, nothing."

He continues to press his lips down my legs, he licks around each ankle in a circular motion. He massages my feet as he nibbles on the heel of my foot, moves to the base and then to my toes; he sucks each one. I lose it! I can't take it anymore. As much as I love foreplay especially the way he goes down. I want him right now. I turn over. "Come here, I need you right now," I whisper. He smirks and continues teasing me. He massages his way up my body and sinks his face into my vagina. I'm weak, my legs spread like butter as he finds heaven on earth. Within moments I cry out:

"Damn, baby, I like that, yes right there! "Oh, my God, oh my God, oh my God Danny! Yes, right there!

"You like that huh?"

"Yes, me likey." The more I scream, the more intent he is on making me cum. He sucks my clitoris and I grant his wish. Oh, my fucking God Dan-nnnyyy! I clutch my legs around his neck and grab his bald head. He's locked in place. I have the tsunami of all orgasms, my nectar showers his face, neck and shoulders. I feel the wetness on the bed. My body jerks like I am being shocked.

I hate that I can't control the jerking, well I can't do anything about it now. Girl, get out your head, now is not the time). I think I've just reached the moon or one of the planets in the galaxy. I'm definitely orbiting. Dang, why is this man's dick so good? Whoo – it's a dick-straction. I refocus on the moment.

I land back on earth and Danny says, "Was that any better or just still alright?"

Heck, I don't even know my name right now. I smirk, my insides warm and tingly.

"I didn't hear you. Maybe I need to put in more work." I quickly respond, "You're a quick study." We laugh. Having expended so much erotic energy on an almost empty stomach, I'm starving and need stamina for the next course. To my surprise, Danny says.

"Get dressed. I need to feed you." I am both relieved and sad. I want him but my stomach aches. I take another quick shower, then Danny hops in after me. When he gets out, I'm dressed and finishing my makeup. He gets dressed and we head to breakfast. After breakfast he drops me off at home. We make plans to see one another in a few days.

Danny is spending the day with his children while I'm going to my parents' house with mine, Cicely and Timothy. Daddy is cooking.

Surprise

Daddy has no clue that plans are underway for his surprise 70th birthday party. Dave, the owner of the Celebrity Club, insists that we host it there. I ask him and the rest of Dad's colleagues to keep it under wraps. My siblings, cousins and I are in cahoots. We plan every detail to the T. We've threatened my sister Raven... she can't hold water. She proudly calls to report that she hasn't spilled the beans. I am actually shocked. I am excited to throw this party for Daddy. The kids and I haven't been in Tulsa to celebrate with him in years.

In the midst of preparations, we're still attempting to keep the party a secret. I conjure up a story to get Daddy to come to the house. I tell him we are taking him to dinner for his birthday and I need him to pick the kids up for me. I tell him he needs to dress up. Telling Daddy to dress up is like telling me to dress up. He loves to talk about every stitch of clothing he has on and how he coordinates his outfit. I instruct Cecily to tell him to stop by the Celebrity Club so she can pick something up.

I meet Dave's son, Steve, at six o'clock to open the building. Luckily, the building is still fully decorated in all its holiday flare. People are arriving with gifts and food and I direct them to the party room. Where are all these people coming from? The parking lot is packed, so I know when Daddy pulls up, he'll figure it out.

Daddy walks in with the largest smile on his face. He must be shocked by how many people are here. I don't think I've ever seen him this happy. Daddy is sharp! Cleaner than the board of health. He holds onto the lapel of his perfectly pressed black suit, with his starched white shirt. A bold floral tie barely budges as he saunters across the floor. The brim on his favorite black fedora with dove-white trim rests on an angle across his forehead. He's tonight's hot topic, all eyes on him. So many of Daddy's adoring fans take pictures, you'd think they were paparazzi. So many people are sharing stories about him and wishing him happy birthday. Look at him... like a kid in the candy store!

Dave's gift to Daddy is a black leather jacket, identical to the one he has on. Daddy quickly takes off his suit jacket and sports the gift for the rest of the night. The sparkle in Daddy's eyes and his permanent smile confirms that he is having the time of his life. He is happy to be celebrated and appreciated. The night is a success. I know I am going to sleep good tonight!

At Will State

FIRED? For what? Am I really hearing this or am I having an out of body experience? No, this shit is real. I'm blankly staring at Sandy the HR Director as she stumbles over her words. It's awkward. I ask, "Fired, for what?"

She can't provide any concrete reason for my unexpected dismissal. Well, unexpected for me. There is no apparent reason why Celine wants me gone. Sandy is visibly flustered, as if she isn't ready to issue the news to me. I'm thinking, *Hell you're not the one losing your job. I am, what are you flustered for? You're good.*

She finally blurts out, "It's a personality thing."

Wait, am I being punked here? Is Ashton Kushner gonna come in with his camera crew? This is bullshit right here. WOW!

"Trudy will explain everything to you." She walks me to her office. Trudy is the HR Generalist and appears just as distraught as I am.

"I'm sorry, I'm really sorry." The wrinkle in her forehead deepens as she profusely apologizes and tries to give me a pep talk.

"You know, I didn't fit in at my last job. Sometimes it's just not a good fit." Her pep talk isn't working.

She continues, "This is just one of those unfortunate things; I'm really sorry. If you need anything, you can call me." Her arm trembling slightly, she hands her business card to me.

"You can use me as a referral. You've done really great work here. You'll get two months' severance pay and we won't deny your unemployment claim." She continues to ramble on about COBRA and some other things. I am still trying to catch my wind.

Do ya'll see this bullshit?

Trudy appears even more distraught than I am – perhaps because she knows that this is a big crock of bullshit and today, maybe she hates her job – who knows.

Then I didn't realize the pattern of working for independent, strong women who were intimidated by me. They saw me as a threat long before I knew my power. They saw it as competition, and they couldn't deal with it. Their intimidation always got the best of them.

From the throes of erotic bliss with Danny, to the highs of Daddy's party, dipshit Trudy drops my ass to the curb. What a buzzkill after the splendor of last night.

Just a few days ago, I was convinced that I could actually make Tulsa work. Life was good, what the fuck just happened? Thinking back, I guess when Celine said that she was the H.N.I.C, that was a warning shot. Today shots fired... direct hit. Six months after arriving in Tulsa I am jobless, without cause. This is at will state shit is no joke; this is some of the craziest shit I have ever experienced.

Question: Have you has it ever felt like you've been sideswiped by an 18-wheeler Mack truck? I mean, has life thrown you a curveball and you wanna throw that bitch back, but it curved so hard it spins you around and you just landed ass-out with no plan B? Well, this is me right now.

Society has us to believe that by the time we are forty we have made it. We have lived long enough to have our lives together and our mark should be engraved in the world. By age forty we are supposed to have been married at least once and had our 2.5 kids, be experts in our fields and own a home with a white picket fence, right? Well, that wasn't my story.

I'm graduating with my master's degree in a few months. They say the third time is a charm, and after what just happened, my life needs charm. Honestly, this break is needed, I've been going non-stop since I've been back in Tulsa. Heck, I'm still shellshocked that I'm even here. Danny calls shortly after I get home. I tell him what happened, so he takes me to dinner. I think I may have had a little too much to drink, okay, maybe way too much. I am experiencing so many emotions at once; the initial shock, then hurt and now the pain of my heart drowning in the Bacardi coconut rum and cranberry juice. Danny attempts to comfort me with words of encouragement, but honestly, I just want to lay down. Actually, I'm horny. I just want him to do me for the rest of the night.

I interrupt him, "Let's go back to your place."

"Are you sure?"

"Yes."

"Well, ok, I figured."

I place my fingers over his lips "Shh, don't figure, just take me with you."

On the way to Danny's, I'm thinking, this is going to be some in mind-bending sex. I'm tipsy and my emotions are all over the place. I'm about to rock his world. I need to get all this frustration out, it's about to go down.

The only thing that goes down is me. Apparently, I was a little heavy on the rum and my ass passed out. I wake up to Danny getting ready for work.

"Well, you had quite the night."

Slightly embarrassed, I say, "Don't remind me."

"Do you want me to take you home now or come back for you at lunch? I cooked breakfast and laid out towels and a toothbrush for you. I know you don't have a change of clothes, but you're more than welcome to put on one of my T-shirts and a pair of sweats."

I want to go home but my head is slightly spinning. I respond, "I'll stay here, you can get me at lunch."

Danny leaves for work and I lay back down. An hour later, I get up, shower and manage to eat a little food. When Danny arrives, I am styling one of his T-shirts, his sweats and my heels. I am a fashion statement...*Still a mess*, Danny drops me off and I prepare for my first day of unemployment. Danny called Cicely last night to let her know I'd be home today. He is thoughtful. Cicely made sure Timothy was up on time and made it to school. I am grateful for her, too.

I guess the drinking and venting helped because I don't skip a beat. I don't immediately look for work. I want to finish school without the responsibility of work, plus I don't know what I want to do. I file for unemployment and apply for food stamps and keep it moving. You would think that being out of work abruptly with no plan would curb my appetite for shopping; it doesn't, it increases because I have so much time on my hands. Plus, I'm in the gym on a regular basis and visit the weight doctor weekly, so you can't tell me anything! I am feeling myself. My daily routine certainly includes shopping, schoolwork, shopping and more shopping. You'd better believe that I am dressed to the nine's every day!

You're probably thinking, girl your priorities are all fucked up. Pat yourself on the back, you're right. I am still a dressed up mess, with just a little less stress than before.

After five years, three attempts and three major changes—graduation day is finally here! This is a major accomplishment! Graduation is held at Union High School, my daughter Cicely's school, and ironically both my niece and I are graduating with our master's degrees. My parents are here, this is the third college graduation that they've attended. They are faithful supporters of all my endeavors. Cicely, Timothy and Danny are also here. No other family members or friends in sight. I am officially a master's degree having, unemployed, government assistance receiving, single, stay-at-home mom. I still look like a million bucks every day.

It's My Birthday

Birthday celebrations are a big deal to me. Over the years I've had elaborate three-day events for my birthday. My friends and family often travel near and far to celebrate. This year is no different. My friends started calling months ago to confirm the date so that they can be here. I'm turning the big 4-0 this year; this celebration has to top all others. The newly remodeled Holiday Inn downtown is the perfect spot! One of my besties, Chasity had her party there in the fall. I like the ambiance and the suites are nice.

I meet with Stanley, the super cool bar manager. He offers the space for free and gives me discounted rates on rooms. I meet the bartender, who's making a drink in my honor, "Sasha Fierce." Stanley and I are in constant communication. This has to be perfect! I show Brittney aka FPL, my oldest and dearest friend the location. She loves it. I leave no detail unturned; everything is confirmed, planned and organized. The theme: A Walk on the Wild Side.

Chasity gifted me a photoshoot last month and I use one of the pictures as my personalized stamp for the invitations.

Don't judge me, I told ya'll I had to do the damn thing. I meant that!

I thank God for creative friends. My girl Mika is super creative and elevates my game. We create tiki hut gift bags; I make personalized candy wrappers with "A Walk on the Wild Side: Allison's 40th Birthday Bash" on them. Cicely helps me wrap each piece of candy. I hire a DJ who will make souvenir CDs for the guests. I ask all the women to wear their favorite animal print.

I find a beautiful Jessica Simpson, teal, strapless, form-fitting dress for five dollars. Mika alters it into a masterpiece, gluing peacock feathers and costume emeralds on the dress. I find four-inch black, satin, jeweled, stacked heels for seven dollars. Mika adds her touch, adding peacock feathers onto them, too.

Oh wee, I can't stand myself!

This silk-based closure and two bundles of Remy Malaysian Hair will set this look off. I change my mind and pair the closure with my Outré First Lady pack of hair. My niece Ivy makes me a flawless wig. I complete the look with hazel contacts, acrylic nails and manicured feet.

It's Thursday and my first out-of-state guests arrive from Atlanta and Texas. We shop, eat, run errands and party at my house. On Friday, guests arrive from Oklahoma City and Dallas. Renee, Trina, Toya and Kim stay with me.

I call the hotel to confirm with Stanley the final details for Saturday. To my shock, I'm told that Stanley's last day was Tuesday—my mouth drops.

"Who's handling my party? We've been planning for months and the party is tomorrow. I have guests from out of state already in town."

"Hold on ma'am." He places me on hold. A woman picks up the phone and introduces herself as Stanley's former boss. I don't care who she is, I just don't want anything stopping my 40th Birthday Bash. The lady explains that Stanley just happened to mention to her on his way out of the door that, "By the way, there is a huge party here Saturday." He did not leave my name, number or any details with anyone.

"I'm happy you called but unfortunately, we are not prepared for your event." I share with her that I've been working with Stanley for months and provide the details of our agreement. She is astonished that Stanley did not share any of the details with anyone. She honors our arrangement. That is all I am concerned about in the first place and am happy and relieved that things are back on track.

On Friday, a small group of us eat dinner at the Cheesecake Factory, then we go to the Aloft Hotel to listen to live music and have drinks, and from there we head to The Living Room Club. Danny is here. He's a regular, in fact this is where we met. It's 2:30 in the morning when we pile inside my tiny duplex. Tomorrow's the big day.

I'm having car issues and I don't have money for the repairs, so I rent a car for the weekend. Quiet is kept, I haven't made a payment since just before losing my job. I don't need any issues on my special day.

Yes, I am reading your mind, you're thinking damn girl, you really are still a mess; and yes, you are right.

Have you ever had a time in your life when it's just off-balance? You look the part, like you have it all together and not a care in the world; you dress it up, straighten it out, and hold your head up, but you're on shaky grounds. Your foundation cracked. The walls are slowly tumbling, about to bury you in your own mess. That's me right now, but I'm about to turn forty. I prop these walls up and keep it moving, at least for the weekend.

I'll deal with it when I have to deal with it, but as for now it's my birthday. Go shorty, it's your birthday, we're going to party like it's my birthday. Don't look at me like that, with your all-judging eye, as if your life has never ever been a mess. If you'll admit it, you've experienced some degree of mess in your life. Your mess may not be my mess, but I'm sure in your own way you've dressed up your mess and some like me are... still a mess.

It's Saturday morning and we're laying around, catching up, mainly recapping what we did the most of last night, some more than others. I don't partake in the "herbal therapy," but some were higher than a motherfucker last night. We are laughing and clowning.

"Damn it, y'all! I forgot to order my cake!" We jump up, pile in the car and go to Sam's Club. Damn, it's too late to order a cake for this evening. I am devastated. My peacock feathers all ruffled. Luckily, Trina is a quick and creative thinker who exemplifies grace under pressure. She finds a half sheet cake and some animal decorations out of the toy aisle. She asks the bakery attendant to create an animal safari scene and write Happy 40th Birthday Allison on top. Ingenious! The cake turns out perfectly, as if was exactly what I had planned all along! Thank God for Trina! She literally saves the day!

We check in to the hotel in the early afternoon and go to our respective rooms. Mine is a suite with a king size bed. We have plenty of food and drinks on deck. Mika meets us to decorate. I'm exhausted and she's irritable, so we bump heads and separate. Renee and Trina step in to finish decorating.

I retreat upstairs to my room. No more drama today. I take a long, hot relaxing shower. The water trickling off my skin is like a gentle massage as I lather with Butterfly Flower bodywash. Excited about what the night will hold, I am grateful that my friends are here to help celebrate. Getting hyped up, I hop out of the shower, dry off, lotion and oil my body, layering myself with Butterfly Flower body spray and Dolce & Gabbana Light Blue perfume. Fruity, sweet, airy and refreshing—just how I like it.

Paying meticulous attention to every detail, I can't let anything slip. I have to look the part. I am *Fabulous and Forty*, and you'd better believe I'm livin' life like it's golden tonight. My individual lashes, mani and pedi are poppin'. I carefully apply makeup, draw the perfect brows, and glide my Black Opal Hazelnut foundation over my face. I top it with MAC NW43 Studio Fix powder. I blend the gold, green, turquoise and blue eyeshadows perfectly, and accent with black in the crevices of my eyes to make my hazel contacts and long lashes pop. Topping my flawless look with my MAC Ruby Woo Red lipstick, I think to myself, *Damn, girl you've got it going on.* I carefully place my human hair bob-styled wig on my head and touch it up with a chi iron. The natural looking part in the silk-based closure is perfect, the jet-black hair is soft and bouncy. I love this look: sophisticated yet flirty, and innocently sexy.

As I unzip the garment bag ever so delicately, I lay the dress onto my arms and slip into it. The teal green complements my chocolate skin. The strapless dress accentuates my shoulders and hugs every crevice and curve of my size eight hourglass shape. The peacock feathers sprawl across the right side and extend past the dress, glimmering off the light. Working out has surely paid off. A few months ago, I was a biscuit away from two-hundred pounds. Now thirty pounds lighter, I look stunning! The peacock feathers spread along the side of the teal high heels as I buckle them. Things are coming together nicely. Lastly, I clasp my favorite Chico's multi-level, oval crystal necklace and put on matching earrings. I laugh to myself; I feel and look amazing. Forty looks damn good on me! I can't wait to see Danny tonight!

I'm ready to party! There's a knock at the door. I walk over and fling the door open. "Happy Birthday Allie Cat Delana!" she blurts out. We hug. The hallway is flooded with people, they all pile in. In no time, we're eating, drinking, laughing and talking. More people quickly fill the suite. Somehow Timmy manages to sneak in, enjoying all the attention that the ladies are showering upon my handsome son. He manages to get into just as many pictures as I'm in. He is supposed to be in the room that I have designated for the kids. I made it so babysitting isn't an issue for anyone who wants to be here.

With a knock on the door, our mini party is interrupted by one of the hotel staff: "You have several guests downstairs and there is no one there to greet them." The ladies refill their drinks and clear the room. "Hey Renee, tell the DJ to play 'I'm Coming Out' for my grand entrance." She laughs. I know she'll tell him.

I refresh my makeup, run my fingers through my hair and put on a fresh coat of lipstick. I adjust my girls so that they sit up properly and head to the elevator. It takes a while for it to reach the eleventh floor. I finally enter, push the L button and descend to the lobby. The door opens to a huge crowd of people standing and waiting for me like the paparazzi. I see my cousins, and a couple of my college friends—people are everywhere! I feel like a celebrity. Diana Ross is belting, *"I'm coming out, I want the world to know, I've to let it show"* from the speakers. Cameras are flashing, cell phones are in my face, as I whisk through the crowd hugging and quickly chatting with my guests.

I turn the corner and spot a large, framed photo of me in my cap and gown standing on a decorated pedestal in the middle of the lobby... Chasity's birthday gift. A poster-sized birthday card is on display for guests to sign upon arrival. Other hotel guests enter the lobby and gaze as they try to figure out what's going on. One of them asks Renee if I'm famous. She responds, "She wishes she was!" I greet the guests and take pictures as they arrive and make my way to the bar.

The DJ's jammin' and people are dancin'. I'm chatting with my college girlfriends when someone grabs me around the waist from behind. I know who it is before I turn around. Danny. He smells delectable, he always does. I turn to greet him, he kisses me on the cheek, looks me over and exclaims, "you look good!" He's taking me all in.

"So, do you handsome."

Danny is immaculately dressed, as usual. His sense of style is one of the qualities that attracts me to him. He has on a crisp, designer, white, dress shirt with a brown stitched vest with chocolate colored, embroidered paisleys. His trousers are the same color brown minus the paisleys. His wing tipped brown shoes glimmer. He looks dapper, looking and smelling of wealth. Certainly, a distinctive gentleman. Sometimes I forget he's sixteen years older than I am. He is so smooth, courtly and fine. I introduce Danny to my college girlfriends. He greets them and engages in small talk for a few moments. "Let's dance." He grabs my hand and leads me to the dance floor. I know I'm in for an exciting night.

We dance through countless songs and of course he had some new moves. I am in bliss. We leave the floor, and he dances with my friends without dates, one by on. That's one of the cool things about him. He makes sure that everyone has a great time and that no one is left out. A man's man for sure. I walk around checking on guests to make sure they are enjoying themselves. The place is packed with family, friends and even people I don't know. The bar is open to other patrons and many of them join in our party. It feels funny partying with my now grown nieces and nephews. I have guests from all over Georgia, Texas and Oklahoma. Heck, even one of Chasity's former NFL player friends and his crew dropped in. Truth be told, those brothers are fine! There is plenty of eye candy in here tonight, for both men and women. I'm on cloud nine.

The bartender delivers "Sasha," tonight's featured drink, an exact color match to my dress. It's fruity, strong and served in a Martini glass. Seductive and classy, I love it. Drinks are coming from every direction. I accept a few, but decline most. I don't want to get drunk, and I certainly do not want a hangover tomorrow. Sasha is my alter-ego, a name given to me by my former boss, Jerome, back in my Georgia Head Start days. I am Sasha tonight: ultra-sexy, confident, intelligent, diva with style, grace and sophistication. Sasha owns any room she walks into. A sexual goddess and queen in my own right.

What brings out your goddess? Think of a time when you felt like a sexual goddess. How did you feel internally? What were you wearing? How was your hair styled? Did you have on your favorite fragrance, shoes or accessories?

Danny makes his way back to me. He strokes the small of my back, his touch electrifying, captivating. His eyes cascade over my body from head to toe, beholding every curvature, taking in full inventory, registering it for when we're alone. His look tells me that there won't be much sleeping tonight. His eyes dance like sparkling stars in a moonlit sky as he gazes in admiration. He grins, flashing his perfectly white teeth. He adores me, longs for me.

Men are funny, yet strange creatures to women when we don't know our own power and how it impacts their actions. Apparently, Danny senses all of the testosterone energy in the room and stays near me. He holds me closer as we dance, his hands linger with every touch. Each picture we take, he rubs the small of my back. He knows his touch arouses me and he makes sure I crave him. Without saying a word, his presence lets everyone know that I belong to him and that I'm off-limits, saved for him alone.

It's two o'clock in the morning and we're shutting things down. Surprisingly there are still quite a few people buzzing around. It's daylight savings time weekend, how did that slip my mind? It's actually three a.m. I forgot to get cash for the DJ, all the planning and going on caught up to me, so Danny escorts me to the ATM. Upon our return, the crowd has dwindled. Only those with rooms are milling about. I pay the DJ and take a few last-minute pictures with my girls from Atlanta. I'm ready to retreat to my room. Danny just now confirms he's staying with me. This creates a dilemma because before he got here, I invited Rena to stay over to keep her from driving one hundred miles back to Oklahoma City tonight. During the course of the night, I'd forgotten that I extended the invitation to her. I should have known by the way he's been all over me tonight that he isn't leaving.

The After Party

Thank goodness I have a suite. Rena crashes out on the fold-out sofa in the living room. Danny and I retreat. We enter the room, as Danny locks the door, I rush to the bathroom to freshen up. I'm concentrating on what is about to go down and not realizing that he is right behind me. I'm startled when he puts his hands on the nape of my neck and gently squeezes as he slowly slides his other hand underneath my dress, he whispers, "Turn the water on." His breath feels warm against my neck. The pressure sends a tingle down my spine. I lose concentration.

I catch a glimpse of his warm beautiful bedroom eyes in the mirror. I see that he came to work, there was no doubt about that. He rubs my inner thighs, searching for my vagina. I turn the water on. He works his finger into my honeycomb. I buzz like a bee. My body rocks to and fro and up and down from him fingering me. I damn near lose my balance. I want to collapse, just let myself melt into a puddle. I feel my nectar warming inside me. I try to hold my breath, but it escapes through muffled grunts.

"Remember, we have company in the other room."

"You're the most important person to me, the only one that matters."

He is straight forward which is one of the qualities I love about him. We match up perfectly in this area. My nipples harden, responding to his breath, his hands, his everything!

Danny sensually bites my neck, "make sure the water is warm."

His deep baritone voice makes me even more moist. He unzips my dress and slides it off. His dick is pressed against the small of my back and his finger is inside me. I bite my lip. He plants soft kisses on my neck, then he licks it from top to bottom in circular strokes. I quiver. He slowly turns me around and sits me on the counter between the two sinks.

He leans over and puts the warm water in his mouth with one hand. He moves from my vagina to my nipple with the other. He pinches my erect nipple then makes circles around my large dark areola. He puts my nipple in his mouth, I feel the warm water encase my nipple. A trickle of water escapes and runs down my body. He switches nipples and repeats the unexpected offense on my other nipple. The warm water running down my body excites me. He moves to the center of my chest and sucks it gently, letting the remainder of the water flow down the center of my body. It invades my pubic hair and glides over the top of my clitoris.

He pushes his big hot tongue into my already parted lips until he completely fills my mouth. He plants a series of lava type kisses, and then he sticks out his tongue for me to suck. I oblige. I can taste remnants of the cognac he drank earlier. I love the way we allow our animal instincts to take over. There are no inhibitions.

I don't know how much more of this I can take, I want him inside me now. He knows I want him.

"You want this dick don't you?"

He already knows the answer. I can't let him conquer me now. I don't answer. "It's your dick, take it." He's showing out tonight. However, I am the Queen, it is my birthday and it's my way tonight. I make a funny face and he laughs at me being coquettish.

"You know this is my pussy right...You belong to me." His words pierce my ears.

Something is different about tonight, maybe because it's my birthday. I feel real grown and real sexy...like a goddess. Sasha is definitely in the building! Is this why they say life begins at 40? Danny sets the tempo intentionally and I am dancing to the music, his rhythm, but my beat. After all it is my birthday, and he is my present. Actually, my body is a gift to him... a package for him to open and enjoy.

My legs are getting numb as I'm straddled between the sinks.

"Let's go to the bedroom." He swoops me up. I feel a bit dizzy, perhaps from the drinks earlier or the intoxication of Danny. Either way I feel light, like I am floating. He guides me towards the bed. We reach the edge of the bed and he stops me.

"Stay right there."

He leaves out the room. What the hell is going on here. He has me hotter than July and he takes an intermission. I feel like a volcano ready to erupt and heck I feel my pussy throbbing like it has a separate heartbeat. What in the world is he doing? While I am deep in thought he reenters the room with a bucket of ice. Oh, shit what does he have in mind. He sits the bucket down on the nightstand and stands behind me.

"Close your eyes." I obey. It's funny I want to be both dominate and submissive. I feel a cool fabric cover my eyes. It's soft and delicate. I know that feeling, it's silk. My curiosity is aroused! Things are about to get real.

He slowly kissing down the back my body. The coldness makes me stand erect. The ice is cold and sensual. He focuses on the small of my back and then glides the ice over the two dimples on each side. I am shaking. He spreads my legs, bends me over the bed and slides me forward. He replenishes the ice. His tongue enters; within seconds I squirt my honey all over his face. This seems to excite him. He grabs my ass cheeks and buries his face. Damn, he eats me from behind. The ice melts and the cold water drips down my pussy, he moves effortlessly across my clit. I bite my lip again to keep from making too much noise. I don't want to disturb my guest in the living room, but I'm about to say *fuck it*! She's going to have to get an earful. I place my own hand over my mouth to reframe from yelling at the top of my lungs. I want him in every part of me. All my senses are heightened. He put his tongue right on my G spot and holds it there for a moment; he flicks his tongue across my clit so fast, it feels motorized. He hums, the vibration makes my pussy pulsate. I pray silently that I don't wake this girl up, damn. I'm weak, my knees are wobblingly. I feel myself losing balance. Just as I am losing balance Danny removes his face from between my ass and grabs a hold to my hips to restore my balance. I glance back at him. My nectar is all over his face, shirt and vest. He unzips his pants and quickly steps out of them. He removes his soaked shirt swiftly. He grabs the handkerchief from his vest and gags me with it. Then he slips his dick inside me. I gasp, he releases his soul inside me. I feel his long, hard, thick dick tap the inside of my belly button as if it's trying to attach itself to my umbilical cord. My soul cries out to his, they connect. It hurts but a good hurt. It really does hurt so good. I get a chill then a warm feeling flows over me.

The room is illuminated in bright lights. I see hues of teal, yellow, white and purple lights flashing. What in the world is going on? I think heaven and earth just collided and I am on the ancestral plane. My head is spinning. He's thrusting with everything he's got. His large penis fills all the space in my vaginal cavity. Between the deep breathing and panting I hear the gushy wetness of my Pandora's box. The freedom that we are experiencing is euphoric. I have the motherload of organisms and tap out. Danny kisses my forehead and spreads the comforter over my limp body. I can't move. He cuddles next to me and the earth and heaven return to their rightful places as I lay snuggled in his arms. Happy 40th birthday to me!

BACK TO REALITY

I wake up and peek into the living room to see if Rena is awake. She's already gone. I tried to keep quiet last night and hope we didn't disturb her. Oh well, it was worth it if we did. I was in ecstasy. Danny and I both shower and pick up where we left off. This time I am in control. Danny lays on his back as I straddle him. I plant kisses on his bald head and work my way down his body, making pitstops at each nipple. I'm seductively working my way down, licking the middle of his chest down to his stomach and then I stop. He moans. I playfully kiss round his now erect penis. I lick the base and work my way up the shaft in a circular pattern. I reach the tip and kiss around it. I place the tip in my mouth and ease my way back down, sucking alternately between soft and medium suctions. My mouth is wet. I am engulfed in pleasing him. I grip the base and work my hands and mouth simultaneously. I'm turned on, I feel the wetness between my legs. His body stiffens; he moans. I hear his toes poppin'. I am turned on. I love to satisfy as he unselfishly always does for me. Our escapade is cut short by a knock on the door.

I almost forgot that my friend Renee's mother, Ms. Langston, is cooking dinner for us before they get on the road headed back to Atlanta. I jump up, grab the keys, and crack the door open slightly.

"Hey girl," I say as I hand the car keys to her. "I'll meet you all at my house shortly."

"Um, hum, don't be all day, you know we have to get on the road."

"I won't, we're getting up now." I close the door and return to Danny with the news.

"Renee's mom is cooking dinner for us before they leave, you want to join us?"

I know what he'd rather be doing. "Sure, he says."

"We'd better get ready to go. I owe you."

"You sure do."

"You'll have to drop me off. I gave the keys to Renee so that they could go and pack their things."

We shower, get dressed, pack up the leftover food and drinks, and then head to the elevator. We check out, load the car and drive to my house. When we enter the house, everyone is dressed and ready to roll out. I'm exhausted. On the way to Ms. Langston's, I'm the topic of discussion. They're clowning me. Everyone's laughing and talking about how much fun they had since they've been here. I miss spending time with my girls and am grateful they're here.

Dinner is delicious. Ms. Langston is a source of entertainment. She has us cracking up with her stories. She kicks into full gear once Danny arrives, questioning and quizzing him like she's part of the alphabet boys, you know: CIA, FBI, IRS. I didn't forewarn him about her, but he's handling it well. Two hours have passed and we're still laughing, sharing stories and taking pictures. I feel sad because it's nearing time for my girls to head out. We wrap things up, then head back to my place where Renee, Trina, Toya and Kim load up and head out. I secretly want to smuggle myself back to Atlanta with them.

Educated, Broke & Bougie

As soon as the A-Team pulls off, Cicely insists that she needs to talk to me. "What is it?" I question. "The repo man came by to pick up your car. He says to call him because if he can't get the car today, he's going to have to call the police and get them involved."

My stomach sinks. "What's his number?" I act as if I'm not embarrassed or worried. I walk to my room, shut the door and dial the number.

He answers on the third ring, "This is George."

I tell him who I am.

"Ma'am," he says tersely, "this is my third attempt to try to pick up the vehicle. No one answered the door the first two times. I need to pick up the vehicle today or I am sorry, but I will have to get the police involved. Ma'am, it's not me, it's the company's policy."

I tell him I understand.

"You seem like a really nice lady. I don't want to embarrass you in front of your neighbors. I am willing to pick the car up from an agreed upon location, if that works for you. Can you drop it off somewhere? That way I don't have to come to your house."

We agree that I will leave my 2006 Toyota Solar at a certain apartment a few minutes away from my home at 5 p.m. Cicely follows me in the rental car. I place the keys in the center arm rest and call George to let him know that I dropped the car off. He thanks me and wishes me good luck.

What repo guy is super nice and lets you drop the car off so that you won't be embarrassed by your neighbors knowing your car got repossessed? They say God looks after children and fools and I am a forty-year-old woman.

We drive home in silence. The rest of the day is a blur.

With the financial aid reimbursement check and my pseudo-severance package depleted, unemployment isn't enough. I went from making $4,500 per month to receiving $1208 with unemployment. I'm feeling the loss of income, struggling, depressed, and hate that I had ever moved back to Tulsa.

My job search is long and drawn out. I apply for jobs in Tulsa, OKC, Dallas and even Kansas. Bumming rides and borrowing my dad's car to go on job interviews and shopping is getting old. My nephew Kelly is temporarily living with us. He buys cars at auctions and sells them. When he has an extra car, he lets me drive it until he sells them. I'm in and out of all sorts of cars. As quickly as he sells them, he replaces them.

Lily Pad

Kelly gives me a car to drive on a more consistent basis, a pine-green 1997 Cadillac Coupe de Ville. It's long, old and fragile, but tough, so Cecily names her Lily Pad. One of the few things that works properly in Lily Pad is her heated leather seats. It's 2011 and this summer heat in Tulsa is straight disrespectful. We're experiencing record temperatures of 119 degrees. Hell, it's hotter here than in Phoenix. So, who in the hell needs heated leather seats in July?

The air doesn't work, and the gas gauge is broken. I am playing Russian Roulette with the gas. Every few days I gas up, guessing how much is in it in hopes that it doesn't run out. Every few days one or more of her tires go flat. Lily Pad has electrical issues, so when the car is off the battery still runs. It isn't uncommon for Lily Pad not to start. I carry jumper cables in the back seat with me. I never know when I may have to beg for a jump. It's worse when no one is available to give me a jump. I need a solution. *This* is crazy! Now I disconnect the battery every time I cut the car off. It's embarrassing having to reconnect the battery before I can drive. I look around before reconnecting it, trying to draw as little attention to myself as possible.

Oh, I failed to mention something that I just noticed today, her special feature.... Hmmm, let's say a message. Lily Pad has the word BITCH keyed in the hood and trunk. Well, I honestly don't know if she came from the auction like this or if one of Kelly's crazy ass girlfriends gave it this present. I step outside to leave and have two flat tires and Lily Pad won't start. This raggedy ass car is working my last good nerve. I call

Kelly to help me. While I'm waiting for him, I stare at the word BITCH on the hood. This morning, I take the message personally. On top of having two flat tires and the engine not starting, now Lily Pad is calling me a bitch. I pace the driveway waiting on Kelly to arrive. He's one of those people that tells you he is coming around the corner, about to pull up right now, and he's sitting on the couch with his shoes off. I know, I've witnessed him do it several times. He arrives forty-five minutes later, sits in the car, turns the key in the ignition and Lily Pad starts right up.

He just looks at me and I say, "She hates me! She never acts up when you come. She acts as if to say: "Kelly, I don't know what she is talking about or why she keeps calling you? I am working just fine!"

In this moment, I feel that Lily Pad really *is* calling me a BITCH. I know for sure that I'm calling her one, too!

Kelly follows me to the nearest gas station and puts air in the tires. I put gas in Lily Pad (a.k.a. BITCH). After I gas up, Kelly says, "Call me if you need me Aunty," and with that he's gone on his way. I ran a few errands and went to my parent's house for a while and then back home before the kids got home from school.

QUICKSAND

I've got to come up with something fast. Each month there is more and more month left at the end of my money, and it's weighing on me. I toy with the idea of selling clothes. I do have a keen eye for fashion, after all. I coordinate outfits for friends over the phone and nail it every time. I can do this in my sleep. Mom has begged me to sell the trash bags full of clothes that I give away each year. Most have tags on them or are only worn once. I brainstorm with Chasity. It sounds good and all, but right now selling clothes isn't going to immediately generate the kind of money I need to sustain my family. I'm walking around lavishly dressed yet, slowing dying on the inside. *I am still a mess*. I need a damn job.

I'm interviewing in Tulsa, OKC and Kansas. I have a second-round interview for a Head Start Director position. I borrow Daddy's car to get here. I can't trust Lily Pad to make it around the corner, let alone to another state. I meet the staff and tour the facility, feeling confident that this job is mine. Who cares that it's in Kansas and I don't have a car? I'll worry about the logistics when the time comes. Well, that time never came.

Sometimes I feel like companies already know who they want and only interview to get new and fresh ideas from their candidates – this feels like one of those times. What are your thoughts about this?

Things are rough, managing my family of three on unemployment's $1208 per month. Danny pitches in here and there but has his own battles. I have one month of unemployment left and not a job offer in sight. I'm fighting this sinking feeling with everything I've got but the quicksand is rising fast.

Recipient

I unequivocally hate coming to the food stamp office for my renewal. This whole experience is disturbing - most of the recipients are in here looking like they just rolled out of bed or came in from off the streets. Some are disheveled and reek of a toxic mixture of cigarettes, alcohol and a funk so strong that the stench lingers in my nose. I'm sniffing myself, but I know good and damn well I took a shower and put on deodorant this morning.

I stand in this long ass line and people-watch. There are black, Hispanic, and white women and men, each with their own story to tell. Some of them look like how I feel internally, *a mess*. The average woman has between three to five unruly children pulling and tugging on them or running around aggravating everyone else in line. Some ignore their children and occasionally utters something to the children. In turn they ignore her like she doesn't exist. A few recipients decide to go with the late-night Wal-Mart run option of pajamas, dirty house shoes, and the *who needs to comb my hair when it can stand all over my head* look. At least three of them look like they had a brawl with meth, and meth won! I am standing here sizing them up when we are all recipients — I have some nerve.

I'm lost in my thoughts until I'm interrupted by, "Excuse me, Miss Lady." I look around, realizing that I am "Miss Lady." I look this guy straight in his eyes. "How are you Miss, Lady? I didn't mean to disturb you, but when I see a fine woman such as yourself, I just had to say something." My inner thoughts desperately want to become words.

Really dude, this is the worst possible place on the planet to try to hit on someone. You are standing in a freaking long ass welfare line either applying for or renewing services. The only thing we can do for one another is cook a good meal, but hell we can't do that if the gas or electric is off – No, thanks. I'll pass!

My face must have conveyed what my mouth didn't say. "I'm sorry for bothering you. Let me let you get back to your thoughts."

"Thank you," are the only words that escape my lips.

They call my number. Now, I'm sitting here in the tiny office with the SNAP worker. I'm scanning her office as she reads my renewal application. Her framed Bachelor of Social Work degree is hanging above her desk.

"Master's degree? Wait, you have a master's degree and this was your last salary? What are you doing here? Why aren't you working?" She looks up at me with a scowl on her face. Now she's sizing me up, acting like I did something to her or that I'm asking for her personal EBT card. It totally irks her that I'm applying for food stamps with my name-brand clothes wearing, highly educated, bougie broke ass—if I ain't a dressed up mess. Look who's being judged now.

Matthew 7: 1-2 Judge not, lest ye be judged. For the judgement you pronounce, you will be judged and the measure you use will be measured unto you.

"Do you honestly think I want to be here? Heck, are y'all hiring?" I catch her off guard, but it lightens her tone.

"You don't want to work here, they don't pay nothing."

"It pays more than I am making now."

"You've got a point. We don't have any openings now but check out the website."

"I will."

She approves my food stamps for six more months. "I hope you find something soon."

"So do I. Hopefully I won't need these for the full time."

WASTELAND

My unemployment and food stamps are coming to an end. This is not how I am supposed to be living anyway. I am back home... it's supposed to be a lot easier, right? Hell, I've lived in Atlanta, Dallas, and Phoenix... all bigger cities with a faster pace of life with a much higher cost of living. I managed to live alright in those places. Then why in the hell is it so difficult to live well in lil' ole T-Town? It's my hometown! This should be a piece of cake, but it isn't. I am living in a small 1200 square foot duplex. My home in Phoenix was a 3800-square-foot, tri-level, five-bedroom three-bathroom complex, with a den, living room, two-car garage and a pool. That also came with my nightmare of an ex, Austin, so I should be grateful for my great escape.

We're on top of one another, no more than two people in the kitchen at a time. The petite living room/dining room combo is our only common area. We're suffocating! The thin walls provide surround sound to all my neighbor's business – I know when she and her husband are arguing, and when they make up. I am sure she hears all my business too. The small front yard adjoins my neighbor's yard, and our backyard is a large open field with no privacy.

I hate living in Tulsa! I wasn't ever supposed to come back here. The only joy I have is shopping, and now I can hardly do that. This place sucks, nothing but a vast wasteland. Ugh, especially north Tulsa, the area of town where the majority of the African Americans live. The once striving north side is now landscaped with rows and rows of abandoned and dilapidated houses and rundown buildings. It's a food desert, with only one to two low end grocery stores and a few decent places to eat. Most restaurants on the north side of town are mom and pop establishments, such as Sweet Lisa's, Oklahoma Style Bar-B-Que, Tastee Freeze and The Burger. There is one McDonalds, one Popeye's Chicken and one Sonic, and the further north you go, the fewer options you have. There aren't even any Oklahoma originals like Braum's or Coney Island.

The area is void of large chain restaurants or big box stores, no Walmart, Target or Home Depot, not a single mall or movie theater. There's a lone Quick Trip convenience store at 46th & Lewis. Ironically, the corporate offices are next door to my subdivision, and there is literally a Quick Trip on every other corner in all other quadrants of the city. Most of the city parks and pools on this side of town have been shut down. Limited resources are put into the schools. Heck, most of the schools on the north side are below capacity and are being closed down.

The life expectancy is fourteen years less for residents in the 74126-zip code than any other zip code in the city. Because of this, the Health Department has opened a new branch on 56th & MLK, formerly Cincinnati. Sporadically sprinkled throughout the north side are small strip malls, some tree-lined sidewalks and newly constructed churches. That's the one thing the north side isn't short of. The city invests little for the development and sustainability of the north corridor, yet everyone acts surprised by the crime and murder rates. It's difficult to imagine Tulsa being the home of the historic Black Wall Street. To me, it is more like a black hole. I am trapped, my anxiety is high, and I am spiraling into another depression.

God, please, I need to find a job! Where are you God? Have you ever felt like God has abandoned you? Do you believe that God has not answered your fervent prayers? How does that make you feel? How do you handle things when God was seemingly silent?

The Breakthrough

I've applied for so many jobs, I lose count. Between the rejection letters and cutoff notices, I can wallpaper my entire duplex. Depression wants to be the MVP in my life, but I am determined to keep pressing forward. I apply for positions with Tulsa Public Schools (TPS), Tulsa County Health Department and for a Center Director position of a La Petite Academy in Oklahoma City. I know desperation has set in since I vowed in 2006 that I would never work as a Director of a Child Care Center again. Hmm, funny how being broke and living in poverty will change your mind about where you will work.

Ironically, I am offered all three positions! After seven months of unemployment, I am now in a position to choose where I want to work. My God, thank You for the breakthrough! I accept the position with TPS as a Community Schools Coordinator. The position is new, and I am the first African American in the position. I am assigned to Hamilton Elementary School, a former middle school. Principal Debra Mason and I are a match made in heaven! I am excited about my job. The only setback is that we only get paid once a month, so I still have a long time before I actually get paid.

I am focused more than ever on getting my life together, starting with a car. Lily Pad and I aren't seeing eye to eye. I like receiving a steady paycheck that I can actually support my family on. Paydays look good! I love having several thousands of dollars in my account at one time, but then I hate seeing it dwindle down to almost nothing by next payday. I'm playing catch up from several months of living on the bare minimum.

I'm getting into the groove of my new job, and the ebbs and flows of managing my money. I shop, but not nearly as much. The desire to shop has curbed quite a bit because I need a car. I am still clanking around town in Lily Pad, and Lily Pad regularly lets me down. Kelly comes to my rescue when Lily Pad acts like a BITCH and won't start. Here I am looking like a million and one bucks, and I step out of this big, old ass green jalopy. At stop lights I look straight ahead, dare not to turn my head to the left or right – for someone may notice me in this big raggedy car. While out shopping or running errands, I park in the farthest parking spaces that I can find. It feels like Lily Pad has a big green neon sign flashing right above her to let everyone know that I am driving her. I've mastered the art of getting in the car, popping the hood and barely lifting the hood to quickly connect her battery cables. Who in the world do I think I am, having the effing audacity to be embarrassed by my car when my alternatives are walking or public transportation? I am still a mess, but haven't quite accepted it.

All I know is that this damn AR, she doesn't deserve to be called a CAR, is an embarrassment. I park her in the back of the parking lot at work. One nosey ass teacher, Mrs. Baker, asked me if I drive the BIG, green Cadillac. Initially I just looked at her as if to say WTF you think, then I said "Yes."

She replied, "I thought so."

BITCH, I thought to myself. She and Lily Pad have a lot in common. I can't wait to get me a car, and this incident gives me more ammunition to save.

I save and save and save. I barely shop, rarely eat out, and when I go the bill's not on me. I enjoy having friends over or visiting them. The less I spend the better! Every pay day, I pay my bills first and bank the rest. I am on a mission... I must get a car. Not sure what I want, but I definitely have to get one soon because Lily Pad has to be put to rest! I prefer to pay cash for a car. I do not ever want to have a car repossessed again! Been there, done that—far too many times. I figure I can purchase it outright and never have to deal with a repo man again. This shit is old.

As I start my search, I talk with family and friends about cars. Two of my close friends, Trina and Chasity, have a Lexus. Well, if they each have a Lexus, I'll get a Lexus.

What a way to make a major life decision? Poor decision-making skills will contribute to being and staying a dressed up mess. Have you ever made a decision based on what someone else has? It's called keeping up with the Jones'.

I look high and low, far and wide, in and out of state. I look for private owners and car dealerships. I research, read the Kelly bluebook and compare prices. I decide on an older model Lexus RX 300. I search for what seems like months.

Ode to Lily Pad

Lily Pad is still up to her antics. Today is the final straw. I came home for lunch and on my way back to work Lily Pad starts grunting like Master P. uuuuughh and shaking like a mechanical bull. I'm traveling about sixty miles an hour and Lily Pad is losing power. I swoop across four lanes of traffic and coast around the curve off the next exit. By the time I reach the stoplight Lily Pad is dead. I turn the ignition off and back on to start, but the damn thing won't start. I sit through several lights, waving for cars to go around me. I call Kelly and get his voicemail. I call Kelly three more times, still no answer. Hot tears stream down my cheeks. I call my mother to see if she can contact Kelly and if Daddy is home. She answers no to both questions. I tell her that I'm stranded and hears my sobs. Mom tries to console me. It isn't working. She says she will try to reach Kelly and my dad.

I get off the phone and hear a tap on the window. I look up at an Oklahoma State Patrol Officer. Tears are still streaming as I roll down the window.

"Hi ma'am, are you okay?"

I explain what happened.

"I can push you around the corner to get you away from the light."

I thank him.

He walks back to his cruiser and pushes me with his patrol car around the corner. "Do you need a ride?"

"No, thank you, I am trying to reach my nephew."

"On my way back, I'll check to see if you're still here."

"Thank you."

He leaves.

I call Kelly again, this time he finally answers. I tell him what happened and where I am. He says he was on his way. I hope that he really is and not sitting on the couch, telling me that he's about to pull up. I call the school and speak with the secretary. I explain what happened and that I'll be in when my ride gets here. At that point, I completely breakdown, crying hysterically.

"I hate this car!" I belt out, "I am sick of this big ass raggedy car."

My mother keeps calling to check on me, but I don't feel like talking. Kelly is taking his time. His ass is probably sitting on a couch. It feels like I've been sitting here for hours. Looking in the rearview mirror, I see a I truck pull up behind me. A middle-aged African American man gets out and walks towards the car. He is holding a business card in his right hand. He's interrupting my pity party. I crack the window. He introduces himself as a Pastor Jones from Stillwell, Oklahoma. He offers to assist me. I thank him and tell him that my nephew is on the way.

He says, "I saw when the officer helped you earlier. When I saw you still sitting here on my way back, I turned around to offer help."

"Thank you."

"Do you want me to wait with you until your nephew gets here?"

"No, thank you." I really just want to sit here and feel sorry for myself. He invites me to his church and goes on his way.

Kelly pulls up ten minutes later. He tries to start Lily Pad but she doesn't start. He drives across the street to the Quick Trip to get gas. He returns, pours the gas in the tank and attempts to start her. The engine click-clacks a few times and then dies. Lily Pad is done! Today she is saying to Kelly, look bitch I am not going to start, not even for you.

Kelly says "I'll come back after I drop you off at work and look at her. I'll pick you up after work."

"Just take me home." I call the secretary and tell her I'm not coming back.

Vow of Secrecy

I go into the house, walk straight to my room and grab my laptop. I'm not going to stop looking until I find a car. That night, I did, a 2001 red Lexus RX300 in Carrolton, Texas. Dang, if only I had found this car last weekend when I was in Dallas with Britney to celebrate her birthday. Trina moved to Dallas from Atlanta in June, so we stayed with her. Britney, my classmate Larry from D.C., and his cousin, celebrated their birthdays in Texas. Let's just say my birthday was a kiddy party compared to this party. It was one of the wildest parties I have ever attended. I have been sworn to secrecy to never reveal the details of this weekend, so I will just let you imagine the things that went on... *(Ok, you've gently twisted my arm).* Let's just say it involves hotels, food, lots of liquor, natural healing of the cannabis kind, a party bus, strippers, girlfriends, side chicks, multiple clubs and things I promise I can't mention. Okay, that's enough.

Disclaimer: I do not partake in any of the extra-curricular activities. Consider me the eye-witness news or court reporter that captures all the details and stores them in my mental camera and my cell phone. There is one funny thing I will share. Trina and I were leaving the hotel on our way back to her house. I pull out a wad of one-dollar bills. Her eyes get big and she asks, "Where did *that* come from?" I burst out laughing!

She says, "What the hell, what did I miss?" She looks so concerned and confused like she thinks I stole the money. I can't stop laughing! She starts laughing with me and doesn't know what she is laughing about. I finally say, "Remember, when the strippers were dancing, and the guys and ladies were throwing money at them, making it rain. Well, I was picking up the money that fell on the floor. I've been holding on to this money all night and couldn't wait until we got in the car to tell you."

I am still laughing so hard tears were rolling down my face. Trina's big brown eyes grow even bigger. She says, "Hell nawl, you're just sneaky!" We laugh harder, bucking in our seats and hunching over. My stomach is hurting, and I can barely breathe.

"You want to get something to eat?" I ask.

"No, I'm sleepy."

"Me, too!"

We continue to laugh and talk about the events that unfolded. *This is the first time that I revealed any contents of this evening. You will have to imagine all the other craziness. Remember I've been sworn to secrecy.*

A New Ride

It's the perfect car, the price range and mileage are just fine. I have to finance, but I can pay her off quickly. I call the dealership, but they're closed. Unphased, I wake up early and call the dealership as soon as it opens. I speak with a salesman named Michael. I ask if the Lexus is still available. It is. I explain to him that I'm traveling from Tulsa, Oklahoma, and will try to make it today. Michael informs me that they close at 6 p.m. today and reopen Monday at 9 a.m. "Ok, I'll call you back and let you know if I will be there today or Monday."

"No problem, mam." I make at least ten calls, trying to get a ride to Dallas. Frustrated, I think of another plan. I'll ride the Greyhound bus and have Trina pick me up from the bus station. I call Michael back to tell him that I'll be there on Monday morning. Next, I call Daddy and ask him to take me to the bus station tomorrow. Lastly, I call Trina to see if she will pick me up. They both agree. I probably should have called them before I called Michael. Oh well, it's working out. I purchase my ticket online, tell the kids I'm heading to Dallas in the morning to buy our new car, and will return on Monday. They are happy as I am; they are just as sick of Lily Pad as I am.

Daddy is always on time and is here to pick me up almost an hour beforehand. "Good morning Daddy, I appreciate you." We exchange small talk on the ride to the bus station until he drops me off downtown.

"Thank you, Daddy, I love you."

"You're welcome. Be careful, call when you get there. I love you and good luck." I love my Daddy. I'm forty and still a Daddy's girl. I get my printed ticket and wait for my bus. A voice comes over the loudspeaker that the bus is here. I sit my luggage on the ground next to the other passengers and stand in line.

I sit directly behind the driver, just like I used to do as a teenager when I used to travel back and forth from Tulsa to Duncan, Oklahoma. Greyhound has upgraded since then. Now they got leather-like seats and cell phone chargers on the armrest. I plug my phone in, put on my headphones and escape inside my head during the long eight-hour trip. In Dallas, I call Trina who's already en-route.

I get in her car and immediately belt-out, "Hey YYS," a nickname we've called each other for years.

"Hey YYS," she replies.

"You hungry?" We grab food on the way to her house, chow down, and then I take a long hot shower. We spend most of the night laughing about last weekend, listening to music and dancing until we fall asleep.

Trina gets up early to get her girls off to school and we head to the dealership. I tell her drop me off, but she stays with me the entire time. I ask the receptionist for Michael. He comes out, we make introductions and get to work on the deal. During the test drive, everything works fine. So far so good. After four hours, I emerge with the keys to my new Lexus. I name her Lexy Red Riding Hood.

I say my goodbyes to Trina and head back to Oklahoma. I call my parents to let them know that I'm heading home. Four hours later, I pull in alongside Lily Pad. I give her a look as if to say, you've been replaced. I turn the car off, saunter over to Lily Pad and introduce her to her replacement. Triumphantly, I call Kelly to inform him that he can pick up his keys and his car! Life is getting better!

I open the front door and call out to Cicely and Timothy to come outside and check out our new ride. Both bedroom doors fling open and out pops Timothy and Cicely flying down the hallway barefoot. Timothy belts passed Cicely and races past me. Cicely is right on his trail. I follow them to the car. Both of them are in the car inspecting it. I can tell by the cheesy grins on their faces that they approve.

"I like it." They both say in unison.

"Way to go mom!" They walk around the car smiling and giving their nods of approval. They both sprint to me and plant the biggest bear hug I've ever had. Who knew a new ride would bring them such joy? Heck, who am I kidding we all feel the same way. Talking over one another, they each tell me how much they love the car. Timothy asks, "Can we go for a ride, mom?"

"Sure, let's go to Braum's to get something to eat! The kids go into the house to get their shoes while I wait in the car.

It's Halloween, and they both want to go trick-or-treating with their friends, so we order our food to go. "No eating in my car." On the drive home, both Cicely and Timmy continue inspecting the car and give their approval. At home, we catch up over dinner. I was only gone a day, but I missed them and they missed me. After dinner they get ready to hang out with their friends. Once they leave, I take a deep breath and exhale. I take a long bath and relax until the kids return. Tonight is the first time in over six months that I am confident that when I go outside to start my car in the morning that it will do just that.

Roller Coaster of Love or Lust

Our life in Tulsa is improving. I have a job that I enjoy. The kids are settled – we haven't moved in over a year. I have reliable transportation and my bills are paid. All is well, except my love life. Danny and I aren't really progressing. I am at a point where I want more, and he seems to keep things at bay. Sticking through situations like this is not exactly my strong point. Over the years I've learned to master the flight mode. Maybe it's my Pisces nature. I quickly erect walls and swim away when I sense imbalance or if the relationship isn't growing. We see one another, but it's dissipating, floundering. The visits are few and far between and we barely talk on the phone. The crazy thing is that I love him, and I believe that he loves me, but he won't say it. His silence hurts and I need to hear him say he loves me. The crazy thing is the night of my birthday party, I overheard him telling Toya that he loves me, but he's never said it to me. I must protect my heart at all costs, even if that means swimming away.

It's funny how things turn out. I was so adamant about not dating Danny, and he was so persistent about dating me. He got me, but he doesn't want to fully commit. I want a commitment, who am I kidding, I want marriage. We're on different pages of different books. There isn't a conversation, nor mutual decision, just separation. Breaking up doesn't mean we'll never see one another again. Tulsa is too small for that and we frequent some of the same places and attend some of the same events.

My stomach turns when I see him out with another woman. He spots me, breaks free and comes over to make small talk. I respond cordially. He has no clue that I feel nauseated. If he's out alone like tonight, we dance, have drinks and spend most of the night together engrossed in one another. In a room full of people, it's as if we are the only two people in the world. I can't deny our chemistry. I can't deny him. At the end of the night, I get in my car and follow him to his house. We enter the house through the garage. We are barely in the house when Danny grabs my face and both hands and draws in to kiss me. His strong wet tongue is delicious. Every cell in my body responds. Trust me, it was tasty as hell. I notice that Maxwell doesn't run up to me begging for attention, but I can't break away from Danny's grasp to ask him where Maxwell is. His kiss gets more intense when I glide my tongue across his straight white teeth and grasp his tongue and suck it. He walks me backwards to the bedroom. Our clothes fly off leaving a trail to the room. Before we reach the bed, he stops and drops to his knees. He rips my purple lace panties off. He licks my belly button. I wince. He moves down to pandora and spreads my box with his two fingers on his right hand. He wastes no time sucking my clit. We are insatiable when it comes to love making. Real love, maybe not so much, but physically and mentally we were right as rain. Speaking of rain, my juices drip and I release my flow freely into his mouth and all over his face. That gets him off, he grabs my ass and thrust his face deeper. I am standing here in my black stilettoes gyrating and grinding my pussy deep into his face as he moans melodically. "You're tasty." I hear him but I can't respond. I am concentrating on keeping my balance.

My rain drips faster, my juices are running down his neck, chest and back. I love watching him eat my pussy, and he loves to eat it. I am like wow when was a brother ever gonna come up for air. Me looking at him suck my juices and hearing his sloshing noises takes him to a higher plane and a deeper depth. He is drunk on my juices. I am intoxicated by his touch. I repeatedly say "Yes, daddy yes!" My words motivate him. He clinches my ass tighter. He gasps then slaps my round ample ass until it stings. The tingle made my pussy muscles squeeze down on his face and I explode in a tidal wave. I want more. He obliges, he knows what I like. My legs eventually give out, my knees buckle, and my entire pelvic region collapses on top of his head. His mouth is covered with me. He pulls me down on the floor to him.

"I need be inside of you."

I want him inside, but I really want to suck his dick. His dick is a beautiful piece of art. I want to count the bulging veins in it and put my mouth all over it from the tip of the head to the shaft. I take control. I slide down and grab his dick. He hunches inside my mouth. I take both of his hands and put them behind my head so he can thrust into my mouth just the way I like for him to do. He is huge and I am always eager to play with his dick and watch the way it springs to life and swings back and forth and from side to side in my hands and in my mouth. Giving head drives me insane as much as it does him. My mouth speaks to his dick and his dick answers.

He moans "Oh baby, that feels good."

I look up, he's admiring how I go to work. He can't take his eyes away. We momentarily lock eyes. I let my drool pool onto the tip of his dick and watch it roll down his pole. I catch it with my warm lips before it hits the base of his shaft. He loses his fucking mind. He guides me off the floor and walks me to his bed. He lays me on my back and goes to the edge of bed. He grabs my legs and swoops them up to his chest. He kisses each ankle as he slides my shoes off. He walks his fingers down each leg as he spreads my long legs from east to west. He eases between my legs and enters. My pussy trembles around his long, wide, dick. I gasp as he goes deeper. Our sprits connect. I can tell he feels the connect. I feel the waves of my womanhood encase him. He swims deeper to the bottom of my ocean. I let out a high pitch scream which seems to last forever. My screams bounce off of the ceiling, floor and all four walls. He hits the bottom of my soul and stirs his dick around inside me like I am a hot cup of coffee. I grip the sheets, comforter, anything in reach. I send out and S.O.S, but there is no one here to save me. Tears roll down my face. The intense pleasure feels amazing and hurts. It hurt so damn good. I call out to God!

Oh, God, oh, God, Oh Gooooooooooddd! We meet in heaven as we both reach climax in unison. In the moment, being with Danny and experiencing this magnificent, uninhibited sexual encounter is mind bending. Our insatiable appetite for each other is magnifying. Our lovemaking is as spiritual as it is sexual. I can't disconnect the two. Here is where our souls find a place to be free in a world that often cost us so much time, energy, money and our peace. When we have an opportunity to connect on a level that transcends all that we know, we can't ignore it. It's acceptance, love, and peace. In each other's arms we find justice in an unjust world. When his penis enters my vagina anything that assassinates our character and self-esteem are released. Life's microaggressions like car trouble, overdue bills, or issues on the job masterfully disappear between the sheets. Here in this moment, we release any and everything. We give in to our desires. Who wouldn't want to feel like this? I just met the creator! It is addictive, I don't know how to come off this drug. I don't know that I want to.

By morning I've had at least ten orgasms, howled like a wolf and orbited a few planets. The intoxicating lure wears off as I feel depressed and guilty that I'd made the poor decision to sleep with him once again. The on again off sexual encounters send me on emotional highs and lows. Just when I think I am over Danny, I make the same tragic mistake and on the roller coaster again. The recovery time to get over him is daunting. I long for him, crave him. My body responds to his touch in a way that it has never responded to anyone else. We connect in ways that I don't have the words to explain. I ride on the wave of our sexual expedition for a few days, then the guilt sets in. I cry and question God about why he made me like this, and then I rationalize why my unhealthy appetite for Danny continues. I want to get off this roller coaster, but I don't know how. I have weak boundaries. I feel as if my soul is tied to his and I can't break free. The only reprieve is the attention from another man. I am addicted to love or lust, either way it's exhausting.

KoKoa

This year has had its share of highs and lows, beginnings and ends. I seek peace but rarely find it. This is one of the rare times that I've found it. In this moment there is no dysfunction, no depression. There is a sense of normalcy in our house and in our family. The kids and I get along. Life is good. It is hard to believe that another holiday season is upon us. This year, I leave hosting the holidays to Daddy, and he's is delighted.

On December 8, 2011, our lives change forever—unbeknownst to me—Cicely purchases a puppy online. She has to let me know about her purchase because she doesn't have a driver's license, nor a car to meet the person from whom she bought him. She tries to convince me that the puppy is my Christmas present. We meet a young lady at the Quick Trip nearby to pick up the puppy...the most adorable lil' pup I've ever seen. He is a tiny black and white, three-month-old Shih Tzu-Pooh named KoKoa. He steals my heart at first sight, but I don't admit it. The last thing on earth that our house needs now is a dog. We buy, (correction, I buy) all the dog supplies immediately after we pick him up: cage, bowl, leash and other supplies. When we get home, we let him explore his surroundings and each of us takes turns holding him. He is so adorable and loveable. We surely are going to spoil him.

I wake up at around 3 a.m. and head to the kitchen to grab a drink. I flip on the light and who's looking at me from the living room couch? Propped and poised on top of a sleeping Cicely, none other than KoKoa. He cocks his head to the side as if to say I've been waiting for you, let's play. Just below him on the floor is a sleeping Timothy. These kids, I'll tell you. I could have saved that money.

Atlanta

Driving down I-20 East, the emerging skyline of downtown Atlanta is invigorating. Being in Atlanta is refreshing. I welcome the crispness of the cold winter air. I miss the vibe of the Dirty South. Atlanta has something for everyone... Welcome to Atlanta, where the "playas play." I can hardly believe that it has been over a year and a half since we left! The kids are eager to be back and so am I. We drop Cicely off at her friend Kayla's and Timothy hangs out at Renee's with her boys, just like old times. I cram as many activities as I can in the few days that we're here. I meet Lisa, Barbara and Vanessa, my former Head Start colleagues for lunch at No Mas. It's good catching up with them. I laugh until my sides hurt.

I spend some time with my ex-fiancée, Jamal; by spending time, I mean sleep with. Who knows why I went down that dead-end street again? The next day when we part ways after lunch, I know that was the last time we'd be together like that. *Remember this is a no judgment zone. If you're judgy you may want to stop reading now.*

For Old Times Sake

I bring in the new year partying with Toya and Kim at the Crown Plaza Ravinia Hotel, the first time I've seen them since my birthday. Renee and I galivant all over the city while we catch up. We're sitting upstairs in her dining room when someone knocks on the door. As Renee answers, I can faintly hear a conversation. She returns smiling. A male voice becomes stronger, and I hear him ask her, "What are you up to?" "Catching up with an old friend," she says sheepishly. The man comes around the corner—our eyes lock.

A blast from the past indeed, it's been eight years since I'd last seen her brother-in-law, Mitchell. He looks as if he sees a ghost, apparently Casper the friendly ghost, because a smile spreads over his mouth, exposing his beautiful white teeth. His 6' 7" muscular frame, hazel eyes, and caramel-colored skin looks just as yummy as it had the last time I'd seen him. Damn, he's still fine!

I catch myself gazing and wonder if my mouth is hanging open. I try to pull myself together. Daaaammmnnn, he's still fine. He's just as shocked to see me. His eyes are sparkling as he takes me all in.

"Hey young lady. How are you? I noticed the Oklahoma tags on the Lexus outside, but didn't expect to see you when I came in the house."

I'm giddy. "Hey Mitchell, I'm good. How are you? It's been a while."

"Too long, if you ask me."

I smile at his response. "You look good. I see you're taking care of yourself."

"Where's Cicely and Timmy?"

He rapidly asks more questions before I can respond. His eyes remain laser focused on me. We are both remembering the time, like Michael Jackson. We exchange information and promise to be in touch. He hugs me before he heads out. Mitchell's muscular arms are strong, and he smells enticing. I want to bury my head in his chest, but I reframe. In case you haven't noticed yet, we have a history.

Time flies by, seems just as we'd unpacked and now, we're packing up Lexy Red Riding Hood and heading back to Oklahoma. Timothy, KoKoa and I say our goodbyes and "I love you" to Renee and her family, then leave to pick Cicely up in Powder Springs. The twelve-hour ride home is somber. No one wants to leave, even KoKoa wants to stay in Atlanta. It may be because he ripped his portable cage apart and was allowed to roam freely at Renee's, and the fact that she introduced him to bacon. I really want to move back to Atlanta, but my life is going decent in Tulsa. I can finally see the silver lining. Moving is such a process, so for now we'll just continue visiting.

Mitchell calls while we travel back to Tulsa. I tell him that we were on the road, and he calls several more times to make sure we make it home safely. After a month of talking nearly every day, Mitchell plans a trip to Tulsa. I anticipate his visit, as it has been several years since we've spent any time with one another.

Mitchell flies in today. I planned to be off but have a huge project I'm working on, so I work half the day. I pick him up and we go to the hotel. We are comfortable with one another, as if there was never a lapse in time. We quickly fill in the blanks of each other's lives for the past eight years. Our weekend is jam packed with workouts, dinner at my parents, sex, and visiting Chasity. On Saturday we take a limo ride to dinner at Charleston's and tour the city. We end the night with more sex. Sunday morning quickly arrives. I am reluctant to greet her as I am not ready for Mitchell to leave. I enjoy his company. We were friends for many years before we crossed the line, and we were discreet about our entanglement for years. There is a certain comfort in our familiarity. We shower, have breakfast and leave for the airport. We hug, kiss, and Mitchell is off to Montgomery.

I am not sure what our intentions are or if we even have any. We keep in contact for months, but who are we fooling? With no intentions for either one of us moving, continuing is a moot point. I resume my ritual with Danny.

I am not confident or comfortable enough in my own skin to be alone. The person I need to freely give the love that I so desperately seek is me, but I don't know it. I am still masking my insecurities with other acquisitions; be it clothes or men, they both temporarily fill a void. I am still a mess.

Addiction Is Addiction, Right?

What comes to mind when you hear the word "addict?" Drugs, alcohol, gambling, porn, sex, food. Addiction usually evokes negative connotations. People think of dreams unrealized, hopes dashed, families broken, respect and lives lost. Or trauma, broken hearts, buried emotions, questions unanswered. The weight of addiction is too heavy to carry, especially for the ones that aren't addicted.

Addictions run rampant in my family: alcohol, crack, gambling, marijuana, over-eating, pills. You name the addiction and I'll name the family member. Not me. Since I was a young girl, I was determined to never be an addict: no, not ME! I am nothing like them, I tell myself.

I have too many horrid memories of the impact of addiction on my family. This history is part of the reason I never wanted to move back home. I shouldn't have to frisk family members or hide all my valuables in my own home. Addiction robs the true identity and the integrity of the person you know and love. It will make them steal your class ring, your TV and even rob your child's piggy bank in order to get that next hit of crack. It will make them sell their food stamps and let their kids starve. Addiction is ugly; it makes people curse, fight, become aggressive, stop eating, black out, miss appointments, and lose jobs. They sell their bodies and their dignity. They lie, cheat and steal from the people they are supposed to love. They are only loyal to the addiction. The impact of addiction will have you searching for words to put on an obituary and selecting yet another black dress to attend a funeral. Funerals are the only time I hate getting dressed up.

What about shopping? Is shopping a habit or an addiction? We're just shopaholics—it's fun, it's trendy, it's in: you can buy shirts, mugs, even movies. These are lighthearted treats. Shopping doesn't really hurt anyone, does it? It's different, you can't die from it, it's not illegal and it doesn't affect our health, right? There's nothing wrong with "retail therapy."

Like other women, I wear my shopping addiction as a badge of honor. I share stories about having clothes in every closet and brag about how many clothes I have with tags still on them, or the outfits I've only worn once. Some women hide new purchases from their significant others in some of the most creative places.

We drop names of designers as if we have exclusive access to them. We're label whores, our money or credit cards pimp us into spending frenzies, all for the latest trends. We've proudly put on mini fashion shows for our friends, strutting and parading around our living rooms and sashaying down our hallways like they're our private runways. I keep saying we are in this together, but I mean I. *When does shopping become an addiction?* Is it when I plan my next shopping excursion while I am in the checkout line? Does shopping every day, sometimes multiple times a day, count? What about when I rush to the store thirty minutes before it closes and marathon shop? When is shopping a necessity and paying bills an option? Addiction to ANYTHING is addiction, right? *Be honest, does any of this sound like you? Have you ever been addicted to shopping? Are there times when you shop more than others? What constitutes the need for retail therapy?*

Clothes Equals Love

My love for clothes started at a very early age. My solace came in clothes. My mother loves to look good and loves to shop. She's always immaculately dressed, even if she was just sitting around the house. She wears designer dresses, shoes, purses and perfumes galore. Adorned in silks, leather, wool, cashmere or furs, always dresses to the nines. Her Fashion Fair makeup is flawless, her real nails long, strong and always painted. Her crowning glory is her beautiful shoulder length sandy brown, reddish hair, bone-straight and usually styled in a mushroom or page boy. Her cinnamon skin is clear and radiant. She is beautiful, and I look nothing like her. She exudes outer beauty but is void of inner beauty.

She dresses me nice, her claim to fame. If nothing else, my mother gifted me with a sense of style and a love for fashion. If there was a lack of love, affection, guidance, direction, it is compensated by designer clothes, purses and accessories. The Shopping Channel is the primary program on TV. Orders come to the house daily. Everything that you can imagine is delivered to our house. We are in and out of countless stores: Dillard's, JC Penny, Trippets, NBC, Shoe Warehouse. We frequent every mall in Tulsa, Southland, South Roads Malls, even the nostalgic Northland, as well as Utica Square and Woodlands Hills—and if you know, don't too many black folks go to those two. If it isn't the mall, it's the Shopping Channel, and long before that were the boosters AKA shoplifters that my mother had on speed dial.

Everyone knew that when one or both of the twins pull up alone or with their entourage of flunkies, unloading large garbage bags from the trunks and their backseat—it's on! They're so many bags that it reminds me of freshly raked leaves sitting in a row on the curb on a fall day.

They talk really fast, almost like auctioneers and everything they pull out of the bags is "SHAAARRP!" they say.

"Oh, Darling, that was made just for you." "Come here, turn around, walk over there," shouting out commands like a drill sergeant. "You see that? Now that's goooorrrgeous! Girl, that's bad—ain't that bad?"

They ask anyone within earshot so that they can co-sign, as to further convince Momma to purchase their stolen goods. The twins CUSS and are so proud of their accomplishments. They are always full of stories of how they outsmarted the salesperson in the store. "That Bitch thought she had us, but we had something for her ass.... Didn't we chile?" The other chiming in "Sho did. I swear 'foe God that bitch thought she had us."

I like listening to their entertaining stories just as much as I like trying on the clothes. To be their client is like being royalty, especially if they bring items just for you, delivered straight to your house. You're a BIG spender, money in the bag. So, you know my mom is an A-Lister. I try on outfit after outfit: dresses, suits, pants, leather coats. You name it, they have it. Mom drops hundreds at a time to keep all of us looking fabulous. Heck, she even has an account with them. Dad's check comes every Monday, and they are there like the door-to-door insurance salesman to collect, and of course with more trash bags full of clothes.

So, this is how my addiction to shopping was born. Funny thing is I didn't realize it until now. Clothes are my coverup from anything that hurts. They are my escape from emptiness, loneliness and low self-esteem. I dress it up, whatever the lack was as a child... Guess, Formalaries, Coach Bags, Fashion Fair makeup, Escape and other expensive perfumes dressed it up. Now the brand names have changed: Ann Taylor, Tahari, Calvin Klein, Jessica Simpson, Kate Spade, BCBG, INC International, Rachel Roy, Tina Turk, Gucci, M.A.C., and countless others, but the impact is the same.

My closet runneth over. I am sure that I could give some of the celebrities a run for their money, perhaps some of the B-listers. If I paid full retail value for my wardrobe, I am certain that it is worth well over one million dollars, conservatively. Forty-six black dresses, at least at last count. Who on earth needs forty-six black dresses? I know I've bought more. Two hundred pairs of shoes for two feet! Are they really necessary? It's a problem when clothes and shoes equal love, beauty, protection, care and concern. Thanks to clothes, I receive compliments from strangers and the attention I crave from men. Admiration for my outer shell is a substitute for what I lack in positive attributes.

At the end of each year, I give away large garbage bags full of them just to make room for more. I regularly donate to Goodwill. Before I moved back, my family and friends loved when I visited because they know two things for sure: I am going shopping and if they are with me, and they will be the beneficiary. When I traveled back to Atlanta, I make a point of going to my favorite store. The manager lets me stay after hours because she knows I will drop three to seven hundred dollars. That may not sound like much to some of you, but I'm purchasing high dollar, name brand clothing at deeply discounted prices. So, three hundred dollars on a good day equates to seventy-five to one hundred pieces of clothes. On a holy grail day, it's two to three hundred pieces. The best part about these shopping sprees is seeing the actual retail value on the receipts. I once saved $6,787. I almost had an orgasm right there. For years my mom has said, "You need to sell those clothes and stop giving them away." She doesn't know that I give them away only to make room for more. It's about the thrill of the deal.

Since being back home, my shopping addiction has hit new heights. I shop nearly every day, sometimes even two or three times per day. I shop before I eat. The thought of new clothes is euphoric. The only thing that comes close to shopping is sex. I have a keen eye for beautiful and unique pieces. I glide down an aisle, touching clothes on racks and suddenly a piece calls out to me. I grab it and the song and dance continues. The clothes speak to me, they call out to me –they tell me how much I need them and how good that they will look on me. When they call out, I answer.

I found a $400 dress for one dollar, yes, one dollar! It's strappy, beaded and very heavy... a silvery blue form fitting number cut just above the knees. When I saw the original tag of $400, I do a triple take I squeal out loud with a rush of adrenaline. I can only imagine that if I got high, then it had to feel like this TOTAL UTOPIA. I can't wait to brag about this magnificent find. This is the NBA Finals' Championship; game is tied with one second left on the clock. The clutch shooter from the visiting team scores a three-pointer at the buzzer and nails it. Bonus, the player gets fouled and gets to shoot a free throw – with shouts from angry fans ranting and taunting him – yet he effortlessly nails the free throw.

Nothing but net! Yeah, it's that exciting, and yes, that intense. I've never worn the dress. It hangs amongst a sea of fancy *after-five* dresses, each one with its own story to tell. Some worn once, some maybe worn a couple of times, but a great deal of them hang with store tags still attached, waiting for the opportunity to adorn my body.

Return on Investment

After toying with the idea for over seven years, I decide that I am going to sell clothes. I can certainly use the extra money, especially since I have a car note and insurance now, plus a puppy. I call Chasity to share my idea with her, and she agrees that it's a great decision.

"I did a story once on a lady that sold clothes online. It turned out to be lucrative for her," Chasity said.

"And it beats getting a part time job. I'll be doing something that I love to do and making some money."

"Sounds like a win-win to me."

"I'm gonna sell on Facebook and by word of mouth. I need a name." We spend the next twenty minutes tossing ideas for names around.

"'Closet Freak... that's a cool name," Chas said.

"I like the play on words. That could work, I really do like that one." I grab my computer to check the name availability. "Dang, it's not available."

"Awe, dang Allie."

"I think, I've got it! What do you think about Closet Chic? It's close to closet freak but different. Thinking in terms of someone's closet being stylish and chic, get it 'Closet Chic.'"

"I like it! I really like it."

"Since I am selling both new and resale, what about "Closet Chic & Re-Mix Clothing?"

"I like it!"

"I do too."

"That's it. I've got to go. I've got work to do."

"Congratulations, Allie."

"Thanks Chas, I love you!"

"I love you too girlie, bye."

I immediately pull new and used clothes from my closet. I take pictures of the clothes and post them to my Facebook page under my business name, Closet Chic & Re-Mix Clothing. Within twenty-four hours I make my first sale.

I call my friend Delanyo in Arizona to tell him the exciting news. I show him the "product line."

"Are those clothes hanging over your bathroom door?" There is a hint of disapproval in his voice.

"Yes."

"Ummph. Is that dress wrinkled? What is this black and white thing? I can't even figure out what that is."

"Hey, I've made my first sale."

"Oh, okay, so that's how you want to be represented? As put together as you are, Ms. Coordinator? You'd better take those clothes off your bathroom door and put a sheet or backdrop or something up there and get those wrinkled clothes down. That looks tacky."

D's words stung. He's right, but ouch! We chat a few more moments. My excitement and enthusiasm are depleted with that one call. I know he means well, but that really hurts. I make the post private and don't touch the clothes or pictures for five months.

Addictive Sex

Since deciding not to pursue my clothing business, I have a lot of time on my hands. I'm single, and the kids are busy with their own activities, which gives me more time to concentrate on my other addiction—men! It's as alluring as my addiction to clothes. This addiction is hard to manage as a Christian woman. I've long loved their attention and the attention of their packages even more. Especially the well-endowed packages, and the ones who know how to fully and properly operate it. Receiving the attention of a man is like dressing up in my favorite outfit, I feel whole and complete. I forget the emptiness and loneliness when my legs are stretched around his body with his manhood inside me. As long as I am wrapped in his arms, whoever he is. I'm protected from the hurt or harm of the outside world. My depression subsides, at least for that moment. The emptiness fills with lust, lust becomes love– at least in my head. I have a pattern that I don't fully recognize, but it plays out pretty much the same over the years. I meet him, fuck him, love him, like him, get to know him and often end up hating him, or at least realizing that I don't want him. I swim away, engulfed with guilt and the desire to be a better Christian.

Other times I'd love him, and if it didn't work out and he left, I spiral down the familiar road of depression and self-hate. I don't have a lot of practice loving myself. So when man after man loves my pussy, my hands and my mouth, my body, but not my mind, not my soul or my being—not the person who I am, I fight to love myself. I succumb to self-destructive behavior. I nitpick about all the things that are wrong with me: my thin, soft, dandelion hair, my broad pug nose, my imperfect smile, my hands, my feet, my deep dark skin tone. I scrutinize any and everything that's wrong with me. When the tears of self-hate show up, I have to remember to not go down depression avenue.

I search for love in broken men and end up with a broken heart, a broken spirit and broken dreams. I've tried celibacy time and time again. Once it lasted for six months, another nine. I convince myself that I feel more Christian if I don't fornicate. The problem is it feels more punitive than rewarding. I struggle severely with this religious sin-and-guilt complex. When I go cold turkey, I am irritable, lonely and miserable, and depression sets in. I stay in bed and in my head and am unproductive. I regularly engage in spiritual and fleshly warfare. Eventually I give up on celibacy and one of two things happen. I meet him, fuck him, and he becomes a memory, or I meet him, fuck him, love him and he becomes my next boyfriend... until he isn't. I work hard to reduce the number of these encounters. I do better when I am in long-term relationships, when it is only one him to focus on. Not being married sometimes feels like a curse. I've had two failed engagements and too many exes. How can I change this, God?

Have you ever struggled with guilt and sin? How do you deal with sexual desires as a single woman?

When it comes to sex, we're taught about sexually transmitted diseases and unwanted pregnancies, but we're not taught about the mental and emotional attachments. No one told me about the emotional turmoil that I'd go through when the act is over and I still long for him, crave him and want him, but the guilt of sin makes me feel dirty and worthless, like a jezebel or whoremonger. The internal battle between my needs, wants and desires and what was morally right collides way too often. Guilt sometimes wins, and desires win at other times. I question the yearning desire God placed inside of me. "What is wrong with me? Why did you make me like this? I am so needy with love that I often mistake love for lust or accept lust because it sometimes masks itself as love. I cannot comprehend why something that feels so good is forbidden, or that I will go to hell for fornicating. The more I battle, the stronger the desire. I subconsciously make the decision that my love for sex is greater than my fear of hell. Sex is my weakness. This desire needs to be tamed, but how? How do I tame these flames burning deep inside my core?

I grow stronger and lessen my need to be with Danny. When I see him out, I reject the invitations to spend the night. Sometimes when he calls, I don't answer. Danny's absence means someone else's presence. I adopted the mantra that the quickest way to get over one man is to get with another, and so it is. Between short bouts of celibacy, I find myself with a familiar or new suitor. Eventually the emotional turmoil leads me back to celibacy. While I struggle through the guilt-and-sin complex of fornication and bounce between celibacy and temptation, I indulge in my guilty pleasure of shopping. It's is the one constant in my life. If shopping and fucking were the only two things that I had to do every day, my life would be bliss.

Unanswered Prayers

Psalm 30 states, "Weeping may endure for a night, but JOY comes in the morning." I have the weeping part down, but joy often escapes me. If there is a leading lady role for a WEEPER, I'd nail it. Insomnia again! Ugh, too much on my mind tonight. Today was more than I could bear. The day started normally, waking up rather early for a Saturday. I had plans to have lunch with my friend Cara, take Timmy to get his haircut, and get Daddy's Father's Day gift. Afterwards, I'd chill around the house for the rest of the day and end up cleaning.

As I was in full fledge cleaning mode, I came across a small pile of papers on my floor. I pick up a small piece of paper and begin reading. I am frozen in place. It's a list of prayers, and as I read each one, I feel sad. The list of prayers is from 2005, seven years ago, and not even one of them have been answered. I drift into deep thoughts about the circumstances in my life during the time that I had written those prayers, then sadness quickly turns to angst. I am not Mrs. Lakes, I am not financially stable, I do not own a home, ugh! This is depressing. "*What had I done wrong? Why hasn't God answered any of my prayers?*" I sigh, ball the paper up and throw it in the trash.

I continue cleaning my room, but I can't get the list off my mind. Losing track of time, I rushed to get ready to meet Cara for lunch. I hadn't seen Cara in over a month and am excited about seeing her. Catching up with her is just the thing I need to get those unanswered prayers off my mind. I finish my makeup and check myself in the mirror. *Looking good girl,* I think to myself. *Yes, I approve.* I am about to head out the door when I decide to check my bank account. I want to see just how much I can spend today. According to the automated response, the familiar voice says, "Your account is currently overdrawn by $2.39. Please make a deposit to…" Deflated like the air rushing out of a balloon...those certainly are not the words I want to hear. I press the key to repeat the balance, as if it is going to magically change: "Your account is currently overdrawn by $2.39, please make a.... 'blah, blah blah.'" The words sound muffled like the teacher's voice on Charlie Brown, wank, wank, wank, wank. What am I going to do? Payday is twelve days away. Hell, that feels like twelve months away. I call Cara.

She answers, "Hey, girl, I am on my way, walking out of the door now. I had to run some errands this morning, where are you?"

I sigh, "I have to cancel. I just checked my bank account and it's overdrawn, so we'll have to catch up another day."

"Come on girl. I've got you. One of the errands I ran was to the bank. I unexpectedly found a check that I had misplaced. I've got you, are you dressed?"

"Yes, I'm dressed."

"Then come on! I will see you in a bit."

I reluctantly agree and head to meet her at Tally's Restaurant.

In route to meet Cara, Chasity calls, "Hey Allie, whatchya doing? Come ride with me to Arkansas to see my dad." We take a lot of girlfriend road trips together. We have fun just being in one another's company, and there's rarely a dull moment when we're together.

"Girl, I just checked my bank account. I'm broke. I'll have to pass this round."

"Just come along for the ride. It'll get your mind off things. We'll have fun, you know how we do it. I can use the company and Daddy will be glad to see you! Don't worry about the money. I've got you."

"Thanks, but I'm good." There was no way in the world I was going out of town broke. She continues to plead her case, and I continue to refuse. I'm frustrated and don't feel like doing anything. I am doing good by just joining Cara for lunch. I'm not in the mood to travel or have any fun. There was nothing fun or funny about my current situation, and I just want to process my next moves.

"Chas, I found an old list of prayers this morning when I was cleaning my room. None of that shit has come true, not one. I'm not married, I don't have own a home, I'm surely not financially stable. Damn girl, I feel like such a failure. I'm just sick of this shit Chas, it's the same thing year after year."

This has got to change, but I don't know how. Shit, I'm not seeing anyone, and I don't have any money to shop, I have no fucking outlet. This is so frustrating. I hate that I moved back here. I've got to go."

By the time we ended our conversation, it was clear that I was in a bad place. "Allison, it's going to be OK. I love you girlie. Keep your head up."

"I love you too Chas. Be safe on the road and tell your dad I said hello. Let me know when you get there." I hang up the phone just as I pull into the parking lot at Tally's.

I enter the restaurant and spot Cara sitting in a booth. Cara is radiant, vibrantly dressed in an array of rich colors and adorned with big, bold jewelry. She greets me with her big beautiful brown eyes and her impeccable smile. I met Cara through Chas some years before when I returned to Tulsa, and our friendship flourished. Cara is about fourteen years my senior. Her personality and demeanor let you know what you are saying matters, and that she's listening to you. She has a way of listening to my circumstances and helping me see the brighter side. She is a voice of reason and provides concrete examples of how to approach my problems or goals. Her voice is very calming and reassuring. She is genuine. I see her as a big sis and mentor. We exchange hugs "Hey, DIVA, it's been too long. You look amazing!"

"So, do you, sis. We have to do better." I sit down and we catch up.

We order our food, and I tell her about finding my list of prayers and my frustrations that none of them have come true, and about my financial situation that set the tone for my day. She shared some suggestions about the unanswered prayers, as well what we are to do in the meantime. As our food arrives, we discuss the challenges of staying faithful when it seems that God isn't listening. Cara shares her struggle about losing her husband, the love of her life, and the challenge of raising three children alone.

"I'd love to remarry but the pickings are slim around here. My kids are all grown and none of them live here, I'm lonely."

"I feel you sis. At least you've been married and had that experience. I haven't and I long for it."

"I miss intimacy and sex too."

"I do too!" We both laugh. I know she's serious and so am I.

"My finances are in disarray sis, so I know what you're going through. You're not alone, but I know you're tired of not having enough. I am too," she says.

"I've struggled before, but I didn't expect to struggle so much here."

"You know sis," says Cara, "I've got to get out of Tulsa, there's nothing left here for me. I am ready to go!"

"I remember when we first met in 2005, you were saying the same thing."

"Well, at that time I had the kids to consider. They were still in school. Now the oldest two have graduated college and my youngest is a senior in college. They all tell me, 'Mom, you have raised us, but we are not coming back to Tulsa. Now it's time, live your life. It's about you; do what makes you happy. Tulsa is a slow death for me. It's time for me to go, so I am doing things to prepare to leave Tulsa and join my family out west."

Upon hearing Cara's declaration, I drift into my thoughts. I know all too well where Cara's coming from. I had often felt that my hometown is a vast wasteland, slowing draining the life out of me. When I left Tulsa for Atlanta in 1996, I NEVER planned on returning. I know the challenges of dating with the intent to marry, and the pickings being slim. I knew loneliness and the financial struggles all too well. I am living that same truth. Is this what women in our demographics have to expect? I have similar conversations with other friends: desires for love, marriage, financial stability and an exit plan. In Tulsa, the outlook is bleak at best.

"Cara, I'm leaving too." I told her about the time I had with my abusive ex Austin out in Phoenix and how that pushed me back to Tulsa. "It was never supposed to be for this long. This is it, my breaking point, three years will not see me in Tulsa, Oklahoma. I have to be out of here before August. I'm leaving by July 31st."

Cara and I wrap up our meals, exchange hugs and leave. I get in my car and look at the time. Nearly three hours have passed. I look at my gas gage, nearly on E. Hmm, empty – just how I'm feeling. It was good seeing Cara, but the heaviness of our conversation did nothing to uplift my mood. Our time spent together just made me focus further on my circumstances. I drift into my thoughts…. "Three years won't see me here. I know I've talked about leaving before, but I am for real this time. I am out of here. I hate it here! Living here was supposed to be easy; this is "home." I have lived in three other states. I am worse off here than I ever was in Atlanta, Dallas or Phoenix. *How did I get here? This is not supposed to be like this, why am I in this situation and why won't God do anything about it?"*

Timothy greets me in the garage with a hug: "Ms. Chasity came by looking for you."

"Did she say what she wanted?"

"No, she was just looking for you. She went back to your room and said to tell you she came by." I was pretty sure I had made myself clear about not wanting to go to Arkansas. Hmmm, not sure why she came by, so I will call later to find out. I go inside where Cicely is lying on the couch and watching T.V. We chitchat and I stop to play with KoKoa, who excitedly wags his tail and runs full speed several times around the couch. He looks like a little black and white, shaggy fur ball zooming around the couch. He made a pit stop for water and completes another lap before stopping in front of me. He hops up and down on his hind legs, begging for attention. He lays down and rolls over so I can rub his belly. Playing with him takes my mind off my circumstances for a moment. I stand, grab my purse and head to my bedroom. KoKoa jumps up and follows me.

I sit my purse on the corner of my dresser and notice an envelope with my name written across it. I recognize the handwriting immediately, Chas. This is why she stopped by. How thoughtful. She knew today was tough for me, and she went out of her way to bring me a card before she left. I open the envelope and take out the card. It doesn't take long for tears to stream down my face. Along with Chas' handwritten note is a twenty-dollar bill. I sniffle, wiping my tears with the back of my hand. I sit on the bed, holding the card in my hands, still crying. KoKoa jumps on the bed and stares at me, with his head tilted as if to ask what's wrong. He snuggles next to me, lays his head in my lap and sighs. He looks back at me as if to say, are you going to tell me what's wrong? I stroke his head and down his back. He looks at me again as if to say, Mommy, it's going to be okay. I compose myself, grab my cell phone and call Chas.

"Sup, Allie?"

"Really Chas?"

"I stopped by your house because I was really worried about you. I could tell you were hurting when we were on the phone earlier, but you weren't there. The kids said you went to lunch with Cara."

"Yes, we made plans a few weeks ago. I called her to cancel after the morning I had, and she wouldn't let me. She said she had me, so I went. That is where I was headed when I spoke to you earlier. When I got home, Timothy told me that you had come by. I noticed your card when I sat my purse on the dresser. It made me cry. You are too sweet and thoughtful."

"Aww Allie, I know what you are going through right now, but it's going to be fine, you just have to trust Him. "You didn't have to give me money, Chas. I would have figured it out somehow."

"Don't worry about it. I know what not having enough feels like."

"Well, it was certainly on time. My car is nearly on E, that is going in the tank." We chat a few more minutes then get off the phone. I lie in bed. My head hurts and is full. I have to figure things out, but for now I just want to be still and left alone. KoKoa snuggles next to me. I think he is worried about me, too. Timothy wakes me up. "What time are we going to the barber shop?"

"You have to wait to get your haircut next week."

"Can I go over to Ms. Chas' house and hang out with Brian?"

"They're gone out of town."

"I'm bored."

"Go read a book or clean your room, and you won't be bored."

"Awe, Mom, you always say that."

"I have to go put gas in my car, you can ride with me."

"Okay." I grab the twenty dollars off my dresser and put it in my bill folder.

We head to Quick Trip Café, just around the corner from our house. I pull into the parking lot, just as the gas pump light on my dashboard illuminates. I hand Timothy my last twenty dollar to go pay for gas.

"Mom, can I have a slushy?"

Did you notice that I just gave him my LAST twenty dollars to pay for gas?

That's the final straw! Crying, I scream at the top of my lungs: "I am *NOT* made of money. That's it; there is no more. You don't appreciate anything!!!! All you do is beg, can I have this, can I have that? I'm tired, I am so tired!"

He just sits there looking at me, confused. His eyes are wide and sad. "I'm sorry, mom," as tears begin to roll from his eyes, trickling down his cheeks, then slowly dripping off the tip of his chin.

Now the guilt kicks in. I begin to sob uncontrollably, and I apologize. "I'm sorry, it's not your fault." At that very moment I feel so low, so lonely. I feel like a failure, defeated. I cannot afford to buy my son an eighty-nine cent slushie. I'm driving a Lexus, immaculately dressed, not a strand of hair out of place, (and until my meltdown) my makeup flawless. I am still a mess.

We sit at the pump, both crying, and me explaining my outburst. My financial situation is not Timothy's fault, and he shouldn't have to take the brunt of my frustration. I apologize again.

"It's okay mom." He has a good disposition, a go-with-the-flow type of kid. He went inside the store, paid for the gas and came back out to pump it. We ride home in silence. I go straight to my room and close the door. KoKoa cries outside my door to get in. I'm not in the mood to play or cuddle.

Cicely knocks on the door but I don't respond. She knocks again. "Mom, are you okay?"

"Yes, you can come in."

She sits on the bed. "Do you need a hug?"

"Yes." She hugs me and asks, "Is there anything that I can do?"

"No, I will be okay." She then says, "Grandpa called, he cooked, and wants us to come to dinner." I don't feel like going anywhere, plus I have to save my gas to get to work. However, I know how important cooking is to Daddy and how offended he'd be if we don't show up.

The kids, KoKoa and I load up and head to my parent's house. They've been in the same house since I was three years old. They're in the den, Mom sitting on one couch and Dad on another watching television. KoKoa runs around the house and makes his way to the kitchen to see what he can beg for.

After eating, I fall asleep watching television and wake up around eleven. When I awake, I find Cicely and Timmy are sleeping, so I gently rub their back to wake them. Dad wants us to take food with us. As the kids are loading the car, my Mom calls me to the den and hands me a ten-dollar bill: "Here's a little change. I'll give you some more on Wednesday." Lying, I tell her I am okay, but she refused to take it back. I put the ten in my purse, hug and kiss my parents' goodbye and head out the door. The ride home is quiet.

It's almost midnight when we get home, I jump in the shower to prepare for bed. I lay in bed, tossing and turning, my mind racing, I replay today's event over and over. I pick up my phone and scan Facebook. After thirty minutes, I put the phone down, lay flat on my back with my right arm bent, the back of my head cupped in my hand. My left arm extends against my side. My right leg is straight, and my left leg is slightly bent. I lay like this for a few minutes. I roll over on my stomach. I started out on the right side of my king size bed now I'm lying in the middle. I extend my limbs. I look like a large X in the middle of a tic-tac-toe game. "Ughhh! I can't get comfortable!" I mutter aloud to myself. I rest my back against the leather headboard. "Lord, I am tired. Please let me rest tonight." I don't know how much time has passed, as I sit desperately seeking rest. Suddenly, I remember to look up information on the guest pastor that is coming to my friend Lea's church tomorrow.

Still A Mess

I visited her church, The Church at BattleCreek, aka the church where I attended a four-week course on relationships hosted by their singles ministry. The course was based on Andy Stanley's *The New Rules for Love, Sex and Dating*. He pastors North Point Community Church in Alpharetta, GA (funny, all the years I lived in Georgia and had never heard of him). Nonetheless, the course was good and very revealing about how Christians as individuals should approach dating. At the end of the course there was a contract that participants had to make with ourselves regarding how we would commit not to date for the next year. During that time, we would work on specific areas that were covered during the course. We did not have to reveal to anyone the areas we were working on.

There were three areas in my life that I wasn't interested in working on at that time. I call them my three F's: Finances, Fornication and Forgiveness. How I see it, my finances are almost impossible to get in order if I don't make more money. I've been looking for part-time jobs and have extended my search outside of Tulsa. Nothing has manifested, so how am I supposed to improve my financial outlook? Hello! Next is fornication… really the dating scene is bleak in Tulsa; I'm sick of being hit on by married men. I'm not interested in being anyone's sloppy second, and I simply don't do married men! How I see it, if you don't like what your wife has to offer, put a wig on her if you want something different! Leave me the hell alone. Okay, that is my soapbox. Now as far as sex goes,

I like sex... no, I love sex, but lately I'm not getting any, except every now and then I hook up with an old suitor to get my fix.

Don't judge... you thought I didn't see you looking all judgy, didn't you?

Though I don't get it on a regular basis, I do not want to give up having sex. I really enjoy expressing myself sexually. Plus, God had not answered my prayers of sending my husband. Remember, if God had done *HIS* part, I would not have to fornicate. I could have all the sex I want with my husband. So as far as I am concerned, I am not ready to work on that F in my life. The third F is forgiveness. That's a really tough one. I've gotten better about forgiving people, but this is still such a challenge for me, especially when I am constantly wronged. No, sorry, not ready to deal with that either. Next! *Well, the contract is with me, and it is my choice what I chose to work on. I am still a mess.*

Oh yeah, back to the guest pastor. At the end of the sermon at the church, on the enormous projector screen, one of the members reflects on the day's lesson and talks about the week to come. The guest pastor for the upcoming week is named Rick Rigsby. This catches my attention because this is a mega church with thousands of members and two locations. Most of the members do not look like me, the African American representation is small, so it caught my attention that Rick, an African American, was their guest pastor. His name is also rather catchy, Rick Rigsby. He has one of those names that you have to say both the first and last night or it doesn't sound as good. The screen shows snippets of his preaching. It seems interesting. The end of the clip reminds everyone that Rick Rigsby would be here next Sunday on Father's Day. I'll make a point to look him up during the upcoming week, and maybe check him out next Sunday.

Well, here it is, nearly 2 a.m. on Sunday, and I still haven't looked up Mr. Rigsby. I Google him, and to my surprise, Dr. Rick Rigsby is an international motivational speaker, ordained minister and author. He was also a former news reporter and college professor. He has even served as a character coach and chaplain for the Texas A&M University Aggies football team. Rick's professional life is amazing, but his story of personal triumph is even more compelling. Rick lost his first wife to cancer at a young age and was left to raise two young sons alone. He went through a period in his life where he was angry with God and rebelled. He shared his redemption story online. I'm intrigued. I really want to see him, so I have to get some sleep. I shut down the computer and get back in bed. Dr. Rigsby and I have a few things in common: I desire to be a motivational speaker, I want to be an author, and I certainly understand his anger with God. There are so many times in my life that God has let me down... so many times where God ignores my pleas and prayers. Maybe God has given up on me. Perhaps He has just forgotten about me. Maybe I have sinned so much that He's turned his mercy and grace away from me.

My mind races. *How did he become a motivational speaker? What made him become an author? Perhaps I will have an opportunity to meet Dr. Rigsby. What if he will be my mentor? Nah, that's crazy thinking. That will never happen. Perhaps I can ask him a few questions, I only need a little guidance and direction. Girl, you are tripping. There won't be an opportunity to meet Mr. Rigsby.* At that point my thoughts turn back over to God. I am searching for answers. *Why don't you love me, God? What have I done so terribly that you just ignore my prayers? I am not the best person on earth but surely, I am not the worst either. I ponder my list of unanswered prayers.*

Why am I not married? Why have You not sent me my husband? Don't I deserve to be someone's wife? Why didn't my ex-fiancée and I work out? What's wrong with me LORD??? I don't have any money; my finances are in the gutter. I don't own my home. Why can't I have happiness? Why, why, why? I realize that I am yelling and crying. I am so tired of this life. Why do You wake me up each morning to keep living this pitiful life? Why won't You just stop waking me up. I am so tired, Lord. I am tired! I am angry and frustrated and lost.

I hear a clear voice say, "THERE ARE AREAS IN YOUR LIFE THAT I AM NOT PLEASED WITH." The voice is so clear that I sit up and look on the opposite side of the bed to see if someone is in here with me. The bed is empty. The covers are crinkled from me tossing and turning. I look around the dark room. There is a slight glare coming from the single window in the room. I am tired, delirious and emotionally drained from today. No, I am exhausted. "HOW DARE YOU QUESTION ME WHEN YOU HAVE AREAS IN YOUR LIFE THAT YOU REFUSE TO HAND OVER TO ME. YOU CANNOT PROSPER WHEN YOU REFUSE TO GET YOUR LIFE IN ORDER. YOU WANT TO BE A MOTIVATIONAL SPEAKER AND HELP OTHERS?" Surely, I am imagining. Perhaps this is all a dream. I get up to turn on the light on to make sure there is no one else in the room, then sit still on the bed.

The voice continues, "YOUR FINANCES ARE IN DISARRY, YOU ARE A SLAVE TO SEXUAL SIN AND YOU REFUSE TO FORGIVE THE PEOPLE WHO HAVE HURT YOU DEEPLY."

"How do you suppose I fix my finances when I can't find a job that will pay me more. I can't even get a part-time job. I have applied for higher lever positions out of state, and I never get the leadership positions. Every time I think that I have gotten to a point where I can start saving, something comes up and wipes me out again. I want a husband and you haven't given me one. Do you think I want to be out here having sex with men that are not my husband? I don't. I want to be married. I don't know how to give up that part of me... you know...you planted it within me. I have desires as a woman to be with a man. Lord, how do you expect me to forgive the murderers who have taken my brothers and nephews from me? How do you expect me to forgive friends and family who have taken them from me? How do you expect me to accept the injustices that I have had to deal with and be okay with things just as they are? I have been praying the same prayers to you for years and you won't answer my prayers. Lord, I am tired of lack! I am tired of constantly being stressed out about money. I am tired, Lord. I am tired! Why do you wake me up each morning anyway?"

"HOW ARE YOU GOING TO GET SOMEONE ELSE'S LIFE IN ORDER WHEN YOUR LIFE IS OUT OF ORDER. YOU ARE STILL A *DRESSED UP MESS*. ON THE OUTSIDE YOU LOOK AS IF YOU HAVE IT ALL TOGETHER. HOWEVER, ON THE INSIDE YOU ARE A MESS. UNTIL YOU GIVE ME EVERY PART OF YOUR LIFE, YOU WILL CONTINUE TO LIVE IN LACK. YOU WILL BE PRAYING THE SAME PRAYERS."

"Wow that is hurtful, Lord." I don't know how to do the things that You want to me work on. I have tried to deal with these issues, and I continue to fail. I am so tired, and at some point, I drift off to sleep.

Have you ever experienced the roller coasters of life and felt that you are stuck on a ride? Have your prayers gone unanswered? Have you ever been angry with God? Has God abandoned you? What did you do? How do you regain your faith?

Divine Intervention

I wake with a sense of urgency. I promptly get out of bed and knock on Cicely's door. "Cicely, time to get up. You are going to church with me this morning and I don't want to be late. Get up now and get in the shower; once you are finished wake your brother up and tell him to get in the shower and get dressed."

I hear her moan something from the other side of the door. Cicely is a very deep sleeper and will wait until the very last minute to get up and get dressed. I knock harder this time and twist the knob, but the door is locked. "I am not kidding, wake up! I need to be on time for church today."

KoKoa whines from the inside of her room to get out. He wants me to take him outside for a walk, but I'm not going to be late to church I need to hear what Rick Rigsby has to say.

In the shower, I reflect on the past twenty-four hours... what a whirlwind. My thoughts quickly jump to the wee hours of this morning, when just a few short hours ago I had the strangest thing happen to me. Was I dreaming or did I really have an encounter with God? Nah, I was probably just dreaming or thinking so hard that my thoughts... umm. I can't explain it. Surely, *I didn't* have an encounter with God. I get out of the shower and quickly get dressed. People dress casually at the church. Pastor Alex Himaya wore jeans last Sunday, and most of the members were in jeans. Still, dressing casually isn't something I'm ready to do yet.

Timothy always says that I am doing too much with how I dress. He thinks I dress to an extreme. I call it style. What does he know anyway? He's just an eleven-year-old kid. I opt for a somewhat casual tangerine summer dress. I slip on brown and tangerine straw-wedged slide-in sandals, and grab my tangerine purse. I put on makeup to match my clothes and meticulously comb my hair. Just as I am finishing up, Timothy comes into my room and is surprisingly ready to go. He gives me a hug. "Are you okay, Mom?"

"Yes, and I'm just about ready to go. Cicely comes in afterwards: "Does my outfit look okay?"

"Yes, you look fine." KoKoa follows Cicely. He does not like to be left out.

We parked on the west side of the building because it was close to the children's side of the church. We log Timothy in and get him settled, then Cicely and I take a long walk to the main sanctuary. The church used to be a mall. The sanctuary is dark. The music ministry has already started singing. It was like entering a concert in progress. This part of the service is different than what I was accustomed to in the Baptist churches that I've attended. There is no choir, choir robes or color coordinating outfits, or hymnals or praise dancers. The band sings contemporary gospel and are displayed on the large screen, along with the words they are singing. It has an urban feel. The glaring lights give off a smoky feel, like steamy dry ice is floating above the members. They are singing a song I had never heard before. Funny how even in the darkness, the ushers are still able to see us and help guide us to our seats. Lea usually sits on the left side, about three-quarters of the way to the back of the church. I look for her, but it is too dark, and the sanctuary is packed. We follow the usher and take our seats. Following along with the words of the song, I am intrigued by how different it is from any music ministry I have ever experienced. The band sings two more songs, concluding praise and worship. One of the ministers comes on stage and urges everyone to applaud for the band and vocalist. Once the applauding ceases, the minister introduces the guest speaker— *finally.* The minister mentions many of Dr. Rick Rigsby's professional accolades that I had read about earlier this morning, and introduces him to the congregation. My heart is racing.

A stout fifty something, Hersey chocolate, African American man enters the stage. He's shaped like an inverted triangle He has a prominent limp and a certain presence about him. From where we're sitting, it's hard to tell just how tall he is. He is bald. His forehead is wide and slopes back, like it ends at the peak of the top of his head. It reminds me of a mountain. His mouth encases an enormous smile. His eyes shine and twinkle, like he has just heard some good news and can't wait to share it. He wears a bluish gray button-down shirt, a brown (looks like suede or microfiber) vest, stone washed blue jeans and brown suede boots. I am excited to finally hear Dr. Rick Rigsby preach. He greets the crowd with a roaring good morning, but the response is solemn. I don't know if it is solemn because they are taking him all in, or if they're shocked that there really is a very large black guy who's going to deliver the sermon today; perhaps they're both curious and afraid. He senses the frosty reception but nonetheless, encourages the crowd: "Come on y'all, you can do better than that! Are you ready to hear from Jesus this morning"? That engages the crowd and a loud applause echoes throughout the church.

He tells us how he ended up in Tulsa on Father's Day to deliver the sermon. He is a joyous and funny man, very entertaining. He shows us the purple polka dot socks his young sons bought him for Father's Day, and exclaims that he knows that it doesn't match a thing, but his sons bought them so he's wearing them. He tells us that he has Oklahoma roots. His mom is from Okmulgee. He cracks a few jokes and then prays over the word before he delivers it. The church has been covering a series on heroes of the Bible. Dr. Rigsby selects Peter, he coins him The Unlikely Hero. I am spellbound while Rick preaches: "Peter is a proud, arrogant, full-of-himself disciple that is in the presence of God and doesn't understand who God is. Peter makes requests of Jesus and does not even know what he is asking for."

As Rick preaches, he talks about how we can be in the presence of God and miss God. We act as if Jesus is our puppet on a string or our granddaddy that winks at us when we sin. Better yet, we think of God as our personal celestial vending machine and that all we have to do is enter a coin and we can manipulate God so he will *always answer our prayers the way we want him to.* He warns us that is not what the Kingdom is about. Jesus wants us to stay connected to him by spending time with him and getting to know him. He warns us to stop looking for a messiah who's going to fill our agenda and to stop looking for a king who is going to be manipulated by us.

Rick then says somebody in here needs to hear this. Have I got a word for you? "In this shallow superficial society we live in, we freak out if our prayers aren't answered." *Is he talking to me?* Rick states how we have the audacity to be angry with God for not answering our prayers when we want him to. "You want to live any kind of way that you desire and expect to be blessed by God. You walk around in your fine clothes, looking good on the outside but on the inside is what matters.

Why is he all in my business? Was it Rick in my room last night?" Is God speaking to me again, this time through Rick?

The sermon is so in line with my life and what I am experiencing, it is as if God invited Rick into my rampage last night. It's as if he is using Rick to confirm that I am still a dressed up mess and that I need to understand who God is. I need to know God.

Rick shares his story of missing God and how he had to clean his closet (his junk) in order to make room for God. He shares his story of personal tragedy, anger with God and redemption. A short video clip plays in the background of him, his first wife and their sons. The video displays the start of their lives together: marriage and kids as well as a very sobering photo of his wife's casket when she passed away of breast cancer. The video shows footage of Rick raising his sons alone and visiting his wife's grave. By the time the video ends, I beg to differ if there was a dry eye in the entire church. Well, my eyes aren't anyway. My throat wells and tears trickle slowly down my face. His story is sad and inspiring at the same time. Rick remarried and had two more sons. He has a blessed life, both personally and professionally, but he had to get to know God on a personal level. Rick shares an array of stories throughout his sermon, including an endearing one about his dad, which makes me think of my own father. He says that his dad is the smartest person he knows and shares some of the life lessons his father gave him. What is intriguing is that Rick's dad was a third-grade drop-out, who had to quit school to work in order to help support the family. Yet, Rick, I mean Dr.

Rick Rigsby, is telling the congregation that the smartest person he knows is his dad, a third-grade dropout. I really want to meet Rick even more than before. I want to let him know how his word has made an imprint on my heart.

When church is over; I see Lea. She, Cicely and I walk out of the sanctuary together. We talk about the sermon and reflect on our thoughts about it. As we enter the café/bookstore area there is an army of people lined up to purchase Rick's book. There must be over one hundred people in line. As we pass the sea of people, I think to myself that I would love to read his book and have an opportunity to meet him. Well, I know the book is out. I simply did not have the money to buy it. We approach the front of the line where Rick is talking and signing books. As Lea, Cicely and I walk pass, I heard someone say, "You're just gonna walk by and not speak." Both my daughter and I turn around as if we are looking for someone we knew. I don't recognize anyone; none of their faces look familiar. I turn back around to continue my conversation, and someone says, "Yes, I am talking to you. You walked right by me and didn't even say hello." I look right in the face of Dr. Rick Rigsby. He is speaking to me! I am thrown off a bit but manage keep my cool, give a small smirk and keep walking.

"Come here, you're not going to speak?" I nudge Cicely to come with me. Lea stays behind. As we walk towards Mr. Rigsby, my daughter says, "He only spoke to us because we're black. We both exhale a light chuckle. We approach Mr. Rigsby, who by the way had a growing line of at least one hundred and fifty people waiting to meet him. He extends his hand, "I'm Rick Rigsby."

I shake his hand. "I'm Allison."

"Who is this beautiful young lady with you?"

"My daughter, Cicely."

He greets Cicely with a handshake. "I come to these big mega churches all over the country and rarely see any black people, and I see three today and the two of you just walk past me like you didn't see me." We all laugh, especially Cicely. Her laugh has a deeper meaning, as if to say see, I told you so. He called us out because we're black.

"Are you all from Tulsa?"

"Yes," we chat a little longer.

"It was nice to meet you Allison and Cicely."

"It's was nice meeting you as well," we say in unison, and then part ways.

WOW, that was weird, I think to myself, as we walk towards Lea. When we approach Lea she says, "Wow that was weird. What did he want?" I tell her about our conversation. We walk together to get our boys from the youth ministry area. Once we get our boys, we chatter a moment and say our goodbyes.

The kids and I walk to the truck. Cicely and I continue to discuss the irony of Mr. Rigsby calling us out and getting to meet him. When we get in the truck, I can't move. I feel both paralyzed and perplexed about the strange string of events that occurred over the last few hours. *What were the chances of me getting to meet Rick Rigsby?* This is crazy. We are still sitting in the parking lot when I realize that I am lost in my thoughts.

My daughter is commenting on what just happened and my son is trying figure out what we are talking about. I explain to Timothy what happened, and we all are saying how weird that was, and kinda funny too. My children don't know how *really* strange this encounter is because they don't know about last night.

Cicely wants me to take her to the mall so that she can purchase a Father's Day gift for her granddad, but she wants to go home to change clothes first. We live less than five minutes away. I put the keys in the ignition and turn the car on, but I can't pull out; something will not let me leave the parking lot. I say to the kids that I really want Rick's book, but I can't afford it. The debate goes on in my head for what seems like hours.

I hear Cicely say, "Mom, I'll buy it for you."

"You don't have to do that." She insists, but I can't let her. I start to feel sad again, disappointed that I can't even afford a ten-dollar book, and the fact that my eighteen-year-old daughter has more money than I do. The thoughts are starting to overwhelm me.

Cicely says, "Mom it's okay, I don't mind. I'll get it for you, I have the money." Just then I remembered the ten dollars that my mother gave me yesterday.

"Oh, I can get it."

I drive around to the south entrance of the church, closest to where Rick Rigsby is signing books. The parking lot has nearly cleared. I leave the kids and keys in the car and walk back into the church. Dr. Rigsby is still talking to parishioners and signing books. With my last ten dollars, I approach a table stacked with Rick's books where two women are selling them, located just behind Mr. Rigsby himself. One of the ladies smiles warmly, accepts my money and hands a book to me.

As she hands the book to me, she asks, "Would like for Rick to sign it?"

"Yes."

She flips to a page in the book for Rick to sign. "Get in line and he'll sign it for you." I walk past Rick to stand in line, which has shortened dramatically. There were fifteen or so people now in front of me. A young lady standing in front of me turns around and excitedly tells me about how much she enjoyed today's sermon, that she is visiting the church and is so happy she came. I told her that I am also visiting and feel the same way. We talk about where we normally attended church and our eagerness to read the book. Our conversation ends with her turn. Standing here, I think wow, this is really strange. How did I end up here? My head is racing with thoughts about the past twenty-four hours. The person in front of me leaves, and I stand face to face with him again. How strange.

"You made it back," Mr. Rigsby said. His hand reaches for my book.

"Yes, I did." First, let me tell you how I enjoyed your sermon. I was visiting the church with my friend last week and saw that you were going to be the guest pastor, so I wanted to come back to hear you preach." I even shared how Cicely said that he spoke to us because we're black, and how funny it was for him to say that is in fact why he spoke to us. We both laughed... I told him how I wanted to meet him but how the line was so long that I just walked by. Continuing to ramble, at some point I share with him how I wanted to purchase his book but didn't have the money because payday isn't until the end of the month, but then realized that I had ten dollars. He says, "Please take the book," but I tell him that I already purchased it. With my book in his hand, he walks toward the table: "Come here for a second. I forgot something over here. I think I forgot my bookmark."

He bends over a stack of books, then waves his hand for me to come closer. "I found it; my book marker is right here."

I walk closer and he hands my book to me. Inside, the bookmark is a ten-dollar bill. This is more than I can take. He doesn't know it's my last ten dollars. My eyes fill with tears and gushes onto my face. All of the heaviness, sadness and confusion from the last twenty-four hours pours out. He must be thinking, ten dollars did all that? Rick stands erect and begins to pray for me: "You are special, and God has great plans for your life as long as you put Him first. Soon, every day will be a payday. God told me to tell you not to worry, trust Him." I just stand here, crying a river. I finally manage to pull myself together and muster the words to tell Mr. Rigsby, "You changed my life."

He has no idea about the personal struggles and my internal chaos. He does not know the sermon was about me, that I am the person to whom he specifically addressed. He does not know that almost every day I walk around well dressed, appearing well put-together, as if there is not a care in the world, but I am bankrupt spiritually and financially. I'm hopeless, and skeletal, wondering every morning why God wakes me up. He does not know that I am still a mess: a dressed up mess, or does he?

Rick signs my book and hands his business card to me. "If there is anything, I can do for you, let me know." I thank him and we go our separate ways. I am yet again drained after this experience. I've done more tear-shedding and snot-slinging in the past twenty-four hours than I have in a long time. I need to get a grip. I walk across the parking lot to my car. The kids are sitting there looking as if they had been there for hours. They both notice that I was crying and ask if I'm okay. I tell them what just happened and how overwhelmed I feel. I sit in the parking lot for a moment to gather my bearings, and eventually drive the short distance home in silence. I'm not in the mood to do much, but I know I have to take Cicely to the mall and then to my parent's house for Father's Day. I'd rather just crawl into bed and start reading my book, *Lessons from a Third Grade Dropout.*

When we open the door, KoKoa sprints around the couch. He really knows how to make us feel special. He has a way of making us feel that we're the most important people in the world. We all change and go to the mall. I take KoKoa with us since we'll be visiting my parent's and he has been by himself all morning. He then runs around the car and jumps into the driver's seat. He scoots over so I can get in, eases his way onto my lap and presses his face against the window. It's his way of telling me to lower the window so he can hold his head out. From the mall to my parent's house, the rest of the day seems like a blur. At home, I prepare for the next day and settle on the bed with my new book. I doze off peacefully.

Closet Chic & Re-Mix Clothing

Less than two weeks after meeting Rick Rigsby, Chas and I are sitting at her kitchen table discussing life. My financial situation hasn't changed much, only that I got paid so my attitude has somewhat changed. I didn't want to be in the same predicament that I was in last month, or in previous months. I want so desperately to break the cycle of living in lack.

"Chas, I've got to make some money. I am really tired of being broke. I've been looking for a part-time job, but nothing has come through."

"What about the clothes. I thought you were going to sell them. Where are the clothes?"

"I still have them."

"Then what's the deal? Just sell the clothes. It will work. What do you have to do to sell them?"

"Prep the clothes, post them and sell them."

"Then just do it. It will work," she repeats.

"I will, I am determined to change my circumstances."

I spend the entire next day and most of the night ironing clothes, dressing them to form and taking pictures with my makeshift backdrop. I edit the pictures, create product descriptions and post them privately. Losing track of time, I finally peel myself from the computer around 2:30

a.m. The next day, after work I spend the evening the same as I had last night.

Timothy leaves with my nephew Landon to spend the Fourth of July with his family, and Cicely will spend the day with her friends. I have the house to myself and am at peace working with the clothes. KoKoa lays around, watching me as I work. The phone ringing interrupts my flow.

"What's up CCL?" Britney says energetically.

"Working on my clothes. I'm moving forward with selling them, been working on them the past couple of days."

"I wanted to see if you want to go with me to Carla's for a barbeque later."

"Sure, I'll meet you at my parent's house in a couple hours."

I keep working, getting so wrapped up in my work that an hour and a half flies by. Finally, I post the pictures online, freshen up, and KoKoa and I go to my parents. Daddy is barbequing when I come in. I chill with my parents until Britney comes, and then the two of us head out together. I leave KoKoa with them. He looks up and tilts his head at me. I return to my parent's house after a few hours. KoKoa is under the table in the den. "He's afraid of the firecrackers," Daddy says as he scrapes the grill with his spatula, then rubs a hand on his grease-stained Oklahoma Thunder T-shirt.

"He's been under there and won't come out," my mother chimes in.

"Come here KoKoa. Mommy's back, come here baby." He pokes his head from underneath the table and looks at me but doesn't budge. I call him again and stretch my hands out. He slowly crawls from underneath the table, like a Navy Seal staying low. He crawls to me. I pick him up and hold him in my arms. His heart is beating fast. As a barrage of fireworks are crackling outside, he snuggles up to me. My poor baby. I am convinced he thinks he's human. My parents and I laugh at KoKoa. He stays tucked underneath me. With KoKoa finally calm, I give him to my dad so that I can fix a plate to take home.

At home, I immediately check my Closet Chic & Re-Mix Clothing Facebook page. It's getting traffic. People are liking the clothes, so I'm excited. My inbox has messages with viewers inquiring about the pieces and prices. I sell my first item in less than twenty-four hours and respond to each inquiry.

As the days and weeks pass, I sell more and more clothes. People want to know if they're really designer clothes or if they're knock-offs. As if!

"Is that a real Ann Taylor dress for that price?" "Where do you get your clothes from?" "Do you work at a boutique or something?" "I like the name of your company; can I use your name to sell clothes?" I can't believe some of the things people ask. "Yes, that's a real Ann Taylor dress." "I get my clothes from a supplier." "No, I don't work at a boutique. I own the clothes, thanks." "Use my company name? Hell no, you can't use my companies name." What is wrong with people. I know that I better make this legit, so I drive to Oklahoma City to get my business license. I am now officially a business owner, and things are taking off.

I did everything backwards in getting the business started, but it's working. I am making money doing what I love, shopping! People are even inquiring about sizes other than those that are in my closet. Time to expand. I soon move to Cicely's closet and invite my sister Shannon to join me in the business, so I can have access to her closet, too. I am a true proprietor. The years of being a shop-a-holic actually start to pay off – I know what women like and how clothes have the ability to completely alter how we feel about ourselves.

Think about your absolute favorite outfit to wear. What color is it? How do you feel when you wear it? Why did you purchase that outfit? Why is it your favorite outfit? What is your mood when you wear it?

See, clothes do something to and for us; they speak to the core of who we are. I now have two full-time jobs. I spend my evenings shopping, prepping or selling. I am making money. I don't care how I have to get it, I just want it. If that means meeting clients in parking lots, at their jobs or their homes, I am there. I set up a makeshift store at home. Clothes are sprawled all over the living and dining room. I use the kids' bathroom as a changing room. Clothes hang along the shower rod, on the back of my sofa, loveseat and chairs. Countless clients sashay from the bathroom to the living room and pose in front of the mirror. I discover that Closet Chic & Re-Mix Clothing is more than just selling clothes—it's a ministry. Women come to me with their insecurities, their hang-ups about their bodies, and together we work on finding clothes that accentuate what they perceive as their most positive attributes.

"I have never worn a short dress in my life. I have skinny legs." "I can't wear that style. I'm too short." "I have always been self-conscious about my legs and knees. They are really big." "I can't wear heals." "My stomach is too big." "I don't have the shape for that." "What do you have for big girls?" Their insecurities roll off their lips like confessions to a priest.

So many women quickly find reasons as to why they cannot wear a particular style or clothing item. I listen and make recommendations. "Just try it." "Have you ever thought about this style?" "Put it on, let me know what you think. If you don't like it, don't buy it."

What makes Closet Chic & Re-Mic Clothing work is that I don't try to sell clothes, although I know that sounds odd. I don't push clothes on people. It isn't about just selling clothes, it is genuinely about helping women look and feel good about themselves. I am impacting lives in a positive way. I adapt the taglines. "Every woman has a runway model inside of you, let me help you bring yours out," and, "We dress the outside and address the inside."

I listen to countless stories of women's struggles with weight, internal noise, and body image. Some carry these messages from childhood into adulthood, and it has a profound impact on their clothing. I have an easy concept: clothes should make you feel like you want to dance. If you feel good and embody what you are wearing, then you are winning. I literally see women transform before my eyes. They come into my house one way, some carrying the weight of the day or of life; however, once they release and try on a piece that I recommend, they emerge a different individual. Their walk changes, their shoulders stand broader, some smile and put on makeup or lipstick. "Oh, I never thought I could wear anything like this, thank you Ms. Allison. We hug and chat, and they leave happy! One of the questions I often get, "Do you have anything for big girls, plus size women or women's world?" I cringe, and my response is always the same: "No."

"Are you discriminating against us?"

"No, I carry sizes 0–5X. What does plus size mean anyway, you plus another person? What is women's world? It has to be a man to come up with that title, no woman in her right mind would say she was as big as the world. I have curvy chic's; you just have more curves than some of us. "If you are satisfied with your curves, own them, if not, do something about it, but only on your terms. Now what can I get you in curvy chics?" The response is often, "Oh, I like that Ms. Allison, curvy chicks.

As the popularity of my business grows, so does my happiness. I am doing what I absolutely love to do, shop and dress women. Every woman deserves to look and feel great about herself; that is how I run Closet Chic, with love and appreciation for all women and all body types and sizes. Closet Chic & Re-Mix Clothing is a labor of love. Staying up around the clock to work with clothes doesn't seem like work at all, it's euphoric. My business is taking off faster than I expected, the word is spreading. I gain the attention of a local singer and am now her stylist for her shows. She refers clients to me at every opportunity, plugs my business on Facebook, invites me to her shows, and calls me on stage to promote my business. Sharon is a Godsend.

Today Sharon invites me to her job to bring clothes for her colleagues to see. She meets me outside along with four of her co-workers and they escort me inside. Women come from every direction to look at the clothes. "I saw the outfit she had on at her show, do you have another dress like that?" "I liked the one she gave to her back-up singer," exclaims another, "with the one sleeve, can you get one of those for me?" They are excited to meet me and I am excited to gain more clients. I explain to them that I hand-select each piece and that I generally don't buy many duplicates. "My pieces aren't one-of-a-kind but most likely you won't see many people walking around looking like you. I like unique, high-quality pieces. If I don't have something you like, I'll find something for you."

While all the ladies are gathered around me, there is one that is looking from afar. She looks to be in her late fifties or early sixties. She watches the crowd and studies me. I see her from the corner of my eye, and we lock eyes a few times. As the women file back to work, she sticks around, eventually comes over and says, "You're a woman of God, aren't you?"

"Yes ma'am, I am."

"I can tell. I know you saw me watching you, didn't you?"

"Yes ma'am, I did." She reminds me of the actress Jenifer Lewis, with a similar facial structure, tone of voice and demeanor.

"I didn't want to be part of the crowd, but I watched you and how you interacted with everyone. I need an outfit for our church revival. I have to look good when I preach."

"Let me know your size and what you are looking for. If I don't already have something, I will personally shop for you. You can come to my house to look if you'd like."

"I prefer to do that. I will have my daughter bring me over."

We exchange information and set a date and time for her to come over. "God is going to bless your business mightily. I see you standing in a room, surrounded by boxes and boxes of clothes. This is going to be big for you, watch and see."

We move to a corner of the room, she takes my hand and begins praying, prophesying over my business. For a moment, I forget that we are in a place of business as we pray and praise God. I could feel the spirit of God's presence. I believe what she says, although I'm not sure how it's going to happen. I've graduated to one small raggedy clothes rack, but I believe her, nonetheless. She is the second person to prophesize over my life in just a few weeks. The next week, her daughter brings her to my house, and she finds the perfect outfit for her revival. Her daughter finds some pieces as well. I am blessed, for the first time in a long time. I am happy, life is good. I am not depressed or battling my personal demons, and every day really is becoming payday.

Rick Rigsby is the guest pastor at church again. I wait eagerly after the sermon to tell him how his words have changed my life. I am so excited to tell him about Closet Chic & Re-Mix Clothing and how my outlook on life has changed. I want to tell him that when we first met, I was contemplating suicide and how I was ready to give up on life. I wait and wait, but I only see a glimpse of him from a distance. I don't get to tell him that my life miraculously shifted since we met. I start to feel a bit stalkerish, so I leave. With his relationship with God, he must know. He wouldn't have shared his message if he didn't have God's ear. I am grateful for his divine intervention.

What About Self Care

Women, especially single mothers, have a devastating habit of taking care of everyone else except themselves. I often forgo medical appointments until it becomes a worst-case scenario. I have an incredibly high tolerance for pain. Perhaps since I have endured so much pain that I've trained my brain and body to just deal with discomforts – whether emotional or physical. I've somehow made myself content with the notion that pain is just a part of life, so when I experience torturous menstrual cycles, I just ascribe it to the fact that I've always had horrific cycles and that they are now just escalating. For several months my cycle gets increasingly worse. My cycles are lasting up to two weeks. I am in so much pain that childbirth seemed like a papercut. The pain feels like a foreign entity is inside of my uterus, an object pulling and stretching my insides apart. Imagine taffy being pulled apart until it is about to rip, and then it's smashed back together again, except the contraction isn't soft like taffy, it is more like being crushed with a MACK truck and a wrecking ball. My cycles are long and heavy, so heavy that I often must use two extra-long pads with wings and a tampon. I change this contraption several times a day.

Another missed day of work, and the inability to do anything but lay in the bed with a heating pad. I refuse to take medication. Mind over matter, I keep telling myself. On most days that works, but today the pain is unbearable, not even Wonder Woman can combat the war on my uterus. This shit is ridiculous. Today I medicate heavily! After a few regimens of pain medicine and hot tea, I sleep for hours.

I'm up early today with a lot of work ahead of me. This period is different, the worst I've ever had. I can feel a large knot or ball protruding from the middle lower cavity of my back. It's hard and grainy to the touch. It's also hot, like a ball of fire. For the average person this invader would have made them to go to the doctor, the nearest urgent care or emergency room, but not me. What kind of fool am I? It is a weird and awkward pain, but Closet Chic & Re-Mix Clothing is growing, my customer base expanding, and the extra money right on time. Work is fine! I am too busy to worry about going to the doctor. I bet you're thinking I'm crazy – right? If you're thinking she's a bat-shit crazy, you're right!

Who can endure such pain without getting checked out? Have you ever forgone a doctor's appointment or ignored a symptom of an illness?

What's even crazier, I don't think that I am crazy for not having the knots checked out. Pain is a part of life, right? I have no time to address this mess. My periods are just tough; it is what it is. I have to keep it moving. Somedays the discharge is so heavy, that no arsenal of pads and tampons can't stop the scarlet red visitor from flowing out of the safety net and onto the beautiful garment that I'm dressed in that day. Despite the heavy discharge, I cannot feel the visitor escape, evade and ruin my clothes. Running errands this evening, a stranger politely walks up to me: "Excuse me, you have something on the back of your dress." I glance down in horror to see that scarlet has yet again messed up my clothes. Embarrassed, I muster "Thank you" and scurry to my car, frantically rushing home to shower, change clothes and attempt to pre-hand wash my clothes before throwing them in the laundry or prepping them to go to the cleaners. This routine is getting old. Maybe I'll try three pads.

I worked the entire summer without taking any time off, and now that school is back in session, it's busy. Busy or not, between working and running a business, I am long overdue for a vacation. I can hardly wait until this staff meeting is over. Today is the last day they will see me for a week. I'm listed on the agenda. "Welcome back teachers, I hope you all had an amazing summer." The principal adjusts her blazer. "We have some exciting initiatives for our families and students." I share details about some of the projects we planned. "I'm glad see all of you back and look forward to an amazing year here at Hamilton Elementary School. Today will be the last day that you all will see me for about a week and a half. I have offsite meetings the next couple of days, and I am taking the week after Labor Day off for some much deserved R&R."

After the meeting, I chat with the principal and a few teachers, then scurry to my office. I am excited to start my vacation, as it had been a long and busy summer. I leave for the day and rush home to start my next gig, tracking inventory, taking pictures and uploading them to Facebook. Tomorrow is a big day. I am being interviewed by Bonita Hassell of the Tulsa World for starting my business from my own closet. Cara set it up, I am so grateful for her; she has been a gem. I spend most of the night entrenched in clothes. I am not sure what time I finally fell asleep.

THE BEST AND WORST DAY

The sun peeks its rays through the mini blinds of my bedroom window, creating a shadow on the wall. I open my eyes and attempt to focus. It takes a moment for my eyes to adjust. It feels like I just fell asleep moments before. I lay in bed thinking about my day. I am elated to be off for a few days. I have a couple of meetings scheduled for the morning, then my interview with Bonita. I pop out of bed and go into the bathroom to start my morning routines. I sit on the toilet to clear my bladder. When I wipe, I feel a huge lump on the left side of my vagina, hmm, strange. "Maybe I am tripping," I mutter aloud, so I wipe again. The large lump is still there. I am not tripping; this is real. Damn, I wonder what this could be. I stand up, wash my hands, brush my teeth and wash my face. I can't shake the idea of the large lump. Well, one thing I know for sure is that it isn't an STD. Danny and I haven't seen one another in a few months.

I take off my gown and stand naked in front of the mirror. My eyes grow wide when I open my legs. The left side of my vagina looked like a lowrider! It is sitting about an inch and a half lower than the right side and is very swollen.

What in the fuck is going on? This can't happen today! I don't have time for this. I grab my hand-held mirror from underneath the cabinet and cock my right leg on the counter. I have to examine this shit up close.

I feel a huge, hard lump about an inch in length. *Damn, what the fuck is this?* Many thoughts rush through my head as I continue to examine my body. The most prevailing thought is I don't have time for this, today is so important. I'll make a doctor's appointment later today for tomorrow. In the shower, my thoughts focus on what I have to do today. I get dressed, but just as I am about to leave the house, I decide I'd better call a friend so I'm not alone today. I have to stage the house for my interview, and this lump is starting to worry me a little. I call in and immediately start working on the house. My friend Angel calls to see what I'm doing on my first day off. I tell her about my interview this evening. "Do you need any help?"

"Sure."

"Ok, I'll come down and help you out. I'll be there in an hour."

"Awesome, bye, I'll see you soon!"

Cicely emerges from her room. I told her about the lump. "Mom, you should go to the doctor!" "I will, but only after this interview." Cicely insists that I make an appointment ASAP, but I ignore her. Wow, I can't believe her. She doesn't understand the importance of this interview. This is going to put Closet Chic & Re-Mix Clothing on the map. I am about to blow up! I can go to the doctor tomorrow. As for today, I'm staging this house and preparing for my interview. I continue arranging clothes on the garage sale rack that I'd bought from my cousin. I arrange and rearrange dresses, pants, skirts and tops on the tiny raggedy rack.

Cicely retreats to her room and slams her door. Not today, nothing is getting in the way of this opportunity. I hear a knock at the door. Angel and I greet one another with a hug. Her hands are full of curtains, pictures and sconces to hang on the walls. "Have your way," I said. She goes to work. We catch up between hanging pictures and sconces, sharing stories about children, work, and of course, men. The house is coming along great. Who knew what a few added touches could do to a place? We vacuum, clean mirrors and dress my form. We talk, eat and clean.

Cicely comes out of her room a couple of times, speaks to Angel and disappears back into her room. She is in one of her perpetual moods and I'm not having it today! "Cicely, come here please!" I yell down the hallway. A few minutes pass and I call again. "Cicely, we need your help hanging a mirror, come here!" Still nothing. "Now I know she hears me! She is about to piss me off!" Angel suggested that maybe Cicely didn't hear me.

"Really, I know she heard me; this place is only so big." This time I scream: "CICELY AUTUMN, come here now!" Cicely flings her door open and storms to the living room. I feel her attitude all over her and all over the room. "Didn't you hear me calling you?"

"I was trying to sleep."

"Sleep, all you do is sleep."

"I'm tired."

"Tired from what? I am sure it's not from doing anything around here! Why are you so tired?"

Cicely gives me one of her looks as if to say, *Fuck you, bitch!* "Why do you have such a nasty attitude?" I ask.

"I don't have an attitude, I'm just sleepy."

"Well, we need your help. We're staging the house for my interview today."

"I don't see what the big deal is."

That was it! I had enough of Cicely's bad attitude and her ungratefulness. What started as a simple request, asking for assistance, had turned into a full-blown argument.

"You act like this bullshit interview is the most important thing in your life."

"Bullshit, really, well this bullshit interview is keeping the fucking lights on. This bullshit interview is going to help grow my business, so you can continue to benefit from it, with your ungrateful ass. I am not up to your shit today Cicely!"

"You're more worried about this than you are with your own health. You're complaining about a lump you found, and you won't even go to the doctor!"

"I told you that I would go tomorrow!"

"Well, that's crazy!"

"Get out of my face Cicely!"

Tears stream down her face. Cicely yells, "I HATE YOU!"

"The story of your fucking life, do you have anything new to add? I am all over the shit about how much you hate me and how I make your life miserable – you don't like it, then get the fuck out! I am sick of your ass any damn way."

"Every Goddam thing that's wrong with you, you want to blame me!"

"Ok, you hate me, so fucking what!"

"You're unreasonable. You are being a bitch!"

I see her life flash before my eyes – before I realize it, I leap towards Cicely. Angel steps in. "That's enough you two! That's it, everybody needs to calm down."

"I'm sick of her nasty ass disrespectful attitude. I've had enough, she has to go!"

"Fine! I'll go!"

"Good, get the fuck out, now!"

We're interrupted by a knock at the door. It's my dad stopping by after work to bring us food, like he does almost every day. I am certain he heard us yelling from outside. I open the door. "Hey, Daddy!" "What's going on?" he asks, "I can hear you all yelling from the driveway."

"I am sick of your ungrateful grandchild!"

"I am sick of your daughter."

"Well, like I said, you can get out!"

Cicely takes off to her room sobbing while Daddy follows her. I am pacing back and forth from the living room to the dining room, my blood is boiling. Of all the days, really, Cicely chooses today to come with this shit. Ooh-wee, I am sick of her ass. She has to go! Poor Angel is standing looking in shock. About ten minutes pass when Cicely and

Daddy emerge from her room. She has a bag in her hand and her eyes are still puffy from crying. Daddy has a bag in his hands as well. KoKoa runs out of the room, trying to figure out what's going on. Daddy shakes his head: "I wish y'all wouldn't act like this."

He and Cicely leave. I am livid. Leave it to Cicely to fuck up my big day and try to turn my Daddy against me. Fuck that shit! I am not having it. Angel looks at me in shock and says, "It will be okay, it's just growing pains. I mutter under my breath and return my focus on preparing for my interview. I am relieved that Angel doesn't ask me about what lump Cicely mentioned.

My phone rings; it's Bonita confirming our interview. We exchange pleasantries, and she lets me know that the interview might be a little later than 5 p.m. since she and the photographer, Scott, will arrive separately. I look at the time, it's a little after 4:30.

"Angel, thank you for everything. I really appreciate you."

"No, problem, I love doing things like this."

"I am going to jump in the shower. The photographer is on his way. Will you listen out for him?" I rush to my room and dash into the shower. As the water pitter-patters on my body, the reality of the moment finally sinks in. Consumed in thoughts, I am going to be in the newspaper. Wow, they are going to do a story on me and how I turned my shopping addiction into a business! Wow, this is an amazing feeling. Closet Chic & Re-Mix Clothing is about to blow up!

The stress of today's events rolls off me like the water and slips down the drain. Relaxed and excited, I am slightly startled to hear my sis Shannon's voice from inside my bedroom: "Hey sissy, whatcha doing?

"Taking a shower. I have a newspaper reporter and camera man on their way to do a story on my business. Cara set it up."

"Oh, that's great!"

"I need to talk to you about your niece, and something else but not until after the interview."

"What's going on?"

"I'll catch you up later."

"Oh, okay, well I just stopped by on my way home from work. I'm going to head to the house. I'll call you when I think you're done."

"Okay, I love you."

"I love you too."

Shannon leaves. I step out of the shower to get dressed. There is no way I am ready to tell her about the lump. She would have flipped out worse than Cicely. I am debating about what to wear. I step into the closet and glance over at least one hundred dresses. I quickly scan my closet. Ahh, perfect, the white raised floral Ann Taylor dress is just right! I slip it on and apply makeup. I select the perfect wig and secure it in place.

The pain in my uterus is becoming unbearable, but I don't want Angel to know that I've been in pain all day and that it's getting worse as the day progresses. I am beginning to feel weak, but I've got to get through this interview Angel calls from the front room to let me know the photographer is here. I glide my lipstick on I emerge into the living room looking like a million and one bucks. I totally transformed; I see the amazement on Angel's face. I walk over to the photographer and he introduces himself, "Hi, I'm Scott from the *Tulsa World*."

"Hi, Scott, I'm Allison, nice to meet you. Bonita called and said that you'd probably beat her here. She should be here shortly."

"I'll go ahead and get set up."

Angel wishes me luck. I smile and thank her as she walks down the hallway to my bedroom. I turn my attention back to Scott.

"Can I get you anything to drink? Water, juice?

"No thanks, I'm good."

"Okay, let me know if you need anything." Just then someone taps on the door. I open the door and am met by a pair of beautiful, wide, brown, round eyes. They look excited and intense. Bonita is caramel-colored, slender and poised, sporting an updated Halle Berry short hairdo. She has very thick hair with strong facial features, a straight nose with wide nostrils and full lips.

"Bonita!" I exclaim.

"Allison, yes, it's good to finally meet you."

"It's nice to meet you as well, come in." We walk over to the couch. Scott and Bonita greet one another and briefly discuss how the interview and photoshoot will take place.

"Would you like something to drink, perhaps water or juice?"

"No, thank you."

I begin to give Bonita some background information about Closet Chic & Re-Mix Clothing and how it all came to pass. She asks a series of questions. At a certain point in the interview, I demonstrate how I help clients find the "right" piece. "Shopping excites me, for as long as I can remember I've loved clothes. It started as a little girl when I would play dress up in my mother's clothes. She had so many clothes and I loved to pretend play in them. I could play dress up for hours. When I shop, it is as if the clothes cry out to me and I answer. When I walk down the aisle, I rub my fingers over the clothes. I love to feel the different fabric textures between my fingers. The bold colors, prints and solids lure me in. I stroll until I connect with the perfect piece. I can feel it and I know it's the one." The interview lasts about forty minutes. Scott takes pictures, I pose for some and others are candid. Bonita and I wrap up the interview and Scott leaves. Bonita stays another twenty minutes to explain next steps. Despite my excitement, my stamina is declining fast, which of course I don't mention to Bonita. The pain is more intense than before, but I do my best to remain focused on our conversation. "Well, I'd better get going. Thank you so much Allison." "No, thank you Bonita. I am both honored and humbled. I will definitely have to thank Cara for arranging this story. It was a pleasure meeting you. I had fun." "It was a pleasure meeting you as well." We hug, and Bonita leaves.

I struggle with each step toward my bedroom, where Angel is on her cellphone. "We're all done!"

"How'd it go?" She tells the person on the phone that she'll call them back.

"It went really well. I am excited! Thank you so much for everything." We walk into the living room.

"Angel, thank you again for spending all day with me and helping me to get the house together. You'd better get home to your family. I'm going to call Shannon to come take me to the hospital. I think my uterus is falling out."

"WHAT?"

"I think my uterus is falling out. I am in a lot of pain. I've been hurting since you got here this morning. I didn't want to say anything."

"So, Cicely was right!"

"I don't want to talk about it, please go home to your family. You've been with me all day!

"Girl, are you crazy? I am not leaving you!"

"Ok, fine, but once Shannon gets here, go home!" I walk to my bedroom, grab my phone and sit on my bed. I call Shannon, but she doesn't answer. I call back, but it goes straight to voicemail. Frustrated and in agony, I call my niece Ivory.

"Hey, Aunt Allison."

"Hey Ivory, have you talked to your mom?"

"Earlier... I thought she came over there."

"She did, but I was in the shower and she had to leave. I need her to come take me to the hospital. I think my uterus is falling out."

"What, wait, what's going on?"

"I'm in a lot of pain. I don't want to call Daddy or Momma because I don't want them to worry. See if you can reach your mom. I really need to go to the hospital."

"Ok, let me see if I can reach her. I'll call you right back."

"Ok, thanks, pray for me. Bye."

"Bye." I dial my sister's number again, still no answer! Angel comes into the room, looking frustrated.

"Allison, I can't believe you haven't said anything all day long!"

"I know, I was focused on the interview. It had to be done."

Have you ever wanted anything so bad, that you'd do anything to get it? Even compromise your health.

I hear a knock, stand up and answer the door. I feel faint and am in excruciating pain, unable to make it to the door independently. Angel answers. I sit on the edge of the bed and can hear Shannon and Angel talk as they walk down the hallway.

"What's going on with you sissy?"

"I'm not sure, I think my uterus is falling out."

"Your uterus?"

"Yes, my uterus. I'm in a lot of pain." My breathing is labored.

"How long have you been like this?"

"All day."

"All day? Why haven't you said anything to anyone?"

I just looked at her, my eyes revealing what I'm thinking.

"Let's get you to the hospital."

"I don't think that I can walk to the car."

Angel interjects, "That's' okay, we'll help you."

"Come on," Shannon instructs, "put one arm around my shoulder and the other one around Angel."

"Where's Timothy?"

"I don't know, outside playing I guess."

"Well, we will worry about him later. Where is Cicely?"

"She's with Daddy. That is what I wanted to talk to you about."

"We got into it today and I put her out. Daddy came over after work and she left with him."

"We'll talk about that later. Right now, we need to get you to the hospital. We're going to take your truck."

"Okay, the keys are on the counter." Shannon grabs the keys as we pass the kitchen. She and Angel help me get in. I hug Angel and thank her again.

From Closet Chic to Hospital Check-In

The ride to St. John's South Hospital is a blur. Dizzy, I plop into a wheelchair and Shannon rolls me to the registration counter, then goes to park the car. She came back as I was checking in. "On a scale from one to ten, what is your pain level?" "Fifteen." I shift from side to side, trying to find a comfortable position - there isn't any. I can barely focus on the questions, but I manage to muster through it. Shannon rolls me to the crowded waiting room. Shannon bombards me with questions, like how long I've been like this and why hadn't I told anyone. I'm agitated because of the pain and can barely tolerate her barrage of questions. "What's going on Allie?" I hear Chasity's voice coming from behind. She walks around to the front of the wheelchair: "What's up with my girl?"

"I think my uterus is falling out."

"Ugh, that's got to be uncomfortable."

"You think?" Shannon raises her voice. "I need to leave and get Timothy and let our parents know what's going on. I'll be back as soon as I can." The nurse calls me. Shannon rolls me to the door, and she and Chasity follow me into the ER wing. The nurse is making small talk, but I don't care to respond. Still, I manage to answer her questions.

We reach a small makeshift room, where the only thing separating me from the next patient are curtains. The nurse starts asking the usual run down of questions. She senses my intense pain and assists me with laying in the bed. She asks if there's anything she can do to relieve some of the pain. Her questions are interrupted by children running loudly and playing just beyond the curtains, exacerbating my pain. The nurse sees the anguish in my eyes and excuses herself to see what's going on. It sounds like a football team and cheering fans, but its young, loud, rambunctious boys who are seemingly oblivious that they're in an ER full of sick people that don't want to hear that shit. The nurse returns and resumes her line of questioning. She battles trying to be heard over the rumbling of footsteps, laughter and outbursts of the three young boys, and she's losing! She excuses herself again. At this point, Shannon says that she'll be back later and leaves.

Chasity stays in with me, thank God! The nurse returns once again. "Ms. West, I do apologize for the interruptions, the patient next to you has three young boys and they are quite rambunctious. I can move you back to the waiting area because I know you are in a lot of pain. I promise I will get you back ASAP! As she speaks, the boys continue to run and scream. I am in so much pain that I am delirious. "Sure, okay, that will be fine."

"I promise, I will get you back as soon as possible," the nurse said. Chasity and the nurse help me back into the wheelchair. The nurse wheels me to the door of the waiting room and Chas pushes me to the seating area. The intensity of the pain magnifies, like two wrecking balls colliding with a MACK truck that simultaneously smash me into a brick wall. My insides are being twisted and grinded. I hadn't felt pain like this since childbirth and honestly, I would welcome the Braxton Hick's contractions... at least they stop. This pain doesn't let up. Ten minutes pass. The nurse emerges and calls someone else to the back. This happens a second time, then a third. Thirty minutes pass and still no sign of the nurse for me.

"Chas, take me to the desk." When we approach the window, I ask why I haven't been called. The intake person rudely states that they have people who are sicker than I am. I explain to her what the nurse told me. She shakes her head. "Well, you should have stayed in the back."

"Chas, let's get out of here. Take me somewhere else." Chas tries to reason with the intake person, but the secretary only becomes ruder. Chas flashes her media badge and tells her that she will hear back from her. She grabs the handles on the wheelchair and whisks me outside. She leaves me on the sidewalk to get her car. A few minutes later, she whips her black Lexus 400 to the ER entrance. She hops out of the car and helps me in. We drive to Hilcrest South which is just a couple of minutes away, across the highway.

"I'll be right back; I'm going to see what their wait looks like. She emerges a few minutes later: "They're packed, it's even worse here." I am leaning my head on the window, unable to sit up straight, the pain unbearable.

"I'll call St. Francis to see what' going on there." I hear her talking but the words aren't audible. I feel like I am drifting in and out of consciousness. When Chas gets off the phone, she says that the wait is over four hours and the last person that they called back has been in the waiting room since 4 p.m. It's 8 p.m. now. I lift my head from the window and turn to Chasity. "Chas, I'll be dead in four hours."

I don't realize how close those words are to the truth. "Alright then, let's get in here. Chas gets out the car and disappears behind the sliding glass doors, quickly returning with a wheelchair. She helps me slump into the chair. It's impossible to sit up straight. Chas whisks the chair around and belts into the ER, and immediately starts talking when she reaches the desk.

"Look, she's really sick and in a lot of pain. We just left one hospital because of poor service. She really needs to see someone - now! I hear the attendant speak to me.

"Hun can you sit up? We have to get some information from you."

I faintly reply "No." Chas jumps in. "No, no she can't sit up. She's in excruciating pain."

"Well, were gonna have to get some information. I'm sorry you're hurting hun."

I give Chas authority to answer any questions and sign any documents on my behalf. "I think my uterus is falling out. It hurts so bad."

Tears flow down my cheeks. I faintly here someone in the background say, "She doesn't have to do all of that, her darn uterus isn't falling out." Pissed, I lift my head to see a tall black woman wearing glasses and a fake ponytail standing a few feet behind the registrar. I drop my head back down, crouching and holding my stomach. "It hurts!" I belt out.

"Hun were moving as fast as we can." She tells someone, "We need to get her back ASAP."

I hear the door open, then someone grabs the handles to the wheelchair and briskly takes me to the back. Chas is still out front, completing paperwork. I am in a small room behind the registrar's desk.

"Can you sit up for me?"

"No, I can't, it hurts to move."

"I need to get your vitals and some blood work. Can you go to the bathroom for me?"

"I don't think so. I can't walk." Tears stream like a river down my face, dripping into my lap. "I am in so much pain. I think my uterus is falling out." I shift to sit up, taking every ounce of energy, I lift my head and stare in the big eyes of the woman that was standing behind the registrar. "You're the one that said that I didn't have to do all of that," my voice scratches, "and that my uterus isn't falling out. You don't know how much pain that I'm in, and you don't know what is going on with me, so I'd appreciate if you'd keep your smart remarks to yourself."

Her eyes bulge. "I didn't say that."

"Yes, you did. You don't think I heard you, but I did. With that attitude you just may be in the wrong line of work. I am not sure what is going on, but I do know that something has dropped down there and I'm in a lot of pain."

She apologizes and takes my vitals. When she finishes, she says, "We're going to take care of you, okay." One thing for sure, the staff is one hundred percent better than the staff at St. John's South. She wheels me into a room and assists me onto the bed. "Someone will be right in," and she walks out.

Chasity comes into the room looking worried. She stares at me for a while, then finally says, "Allie, I hate that you're feeling this way. I don't like seeing you like this. I'm sorry."

"It's not your fault, at least they got me to the back."

"I'm going to have to leave to get Brian soon. I just rushed here after work. Shannon called to tell me that she was taking you to the hospital."

"Thank you for coming. I'll be fine, go handle your business."

"I hate to leave you. When is Shannon coming back?"

"I'm not sure. She went to get Timothy and take him to my parents."

"I'll wait a lil' while longer." The pain continues to intensify. I cry unconsolably. Several medical personnel are in and out of the room. They set my IV and give me pain medication. They want me to try to go the bathroom, or they will have to put in a catheter. I don't want that, so I tell them that I'll try. Two nurses help me out of bed and lead me to the bathroom.

The female attendant holds my elbow and helps lower me onto the toilet, then leaves. Oh God, this hurts. I manage to excrete a urine sample into the cup I call for the nurse to help me return to the wheelchair. "Good job, you did it!" she exclaims, like I am a small child being potty-trained. She has no clue about how the idea of a catheter motivated me. She helps me to the wheelchair and back to my room, where the other nurse joins her to help me back into bed. Chas leaves as soon as I'm secure in bed. "I'll call Shannon to keep track of what's going on. If they keep you, I'll come see you tomorrow. Okay, I love you girlie."

"I love you too Chas." With Chas gone, I'm lonely and scared. The ER doctor introduces himself. "We're running tests on your blood and urine and I've ordered a CAT Scan. While he is talking, a nurse enters and attaches more fluids to my IV. "How is your pain level sweetie. Are you feeling any better?"

"No."

"Really? Let me see if we can get you something else because you should have gotten some relief by now."

I'm exhausted by the pain. To say that today has been a long day would be an understatement. How did the best day of my life quickly turn into the worst day of my life? Both the doctor and nurse exit.

I'm lost in thought when the nurse returns. She injects pain medicine into my IV. "There sweetie, you should be feeling better soon."

"Thank you." As she leaves, another one enters.

"Hi Ms. West, I'll be taking you for your CAT scan shortly." She checks my vitals and fluid levels and disappears behind the curtain. The doctor reenters, "How's the pain level?"

"I'm starting to get some relief."

"Great." He turns his back and looks through my chart. I continue to think about the experience that I had at St. Johns South compared to my experience here at Hilcrest South. Here, the medical team is extremely attentive and seems genuinely concerned about seeing to my medical needs. I want the doctor to know how pleased I am with their level of care.

"Excuse me." The doctor faces me.

"I wanted you to know that I am really impressed with how attentive you all are here and the level of care that I am receiving. I was at another facility before this one and the service was awful, so awful that I left and came here. They got me registered and to the back very quickly, and you and your team have been awesome."

The doctor looks very perplexed. He is a tall, thin man with feathered, brunette hair that ends midway between his neck and shoulders. His horned-rimmed glasses make his small eyes appear even smaller. He has a pointy nose, and a chiseled chin. He looks to be in his late forties or early fifties. He peers through the lenses of his glasses and then just over the top of the lens, then responds. "We're trying to save your life. You're the sickest person we've seen all night. Your white blood counts are off the charts and we don't know how you're even conscious. You're a very sick woman." His words don't completely register.

After my CAT scan, I find Shannon out is in the waiting room. She lets me know that Timmy is with our parents and asks about my results. I ask Shannon to call my principal. She steps out to place the call. People are in and out of the room, running tests, taking blood, checking vitals and administering medication. Shannon returns after speaking with my principal, who is understanding.

The doctor returns, puts his hands in his white overcoat and looks at me with heavy eyelids: "You have several fibroid cysts on your ovaries and an infection. The infection is showing up on the CAT scan, although infections don't usually show up on CAT scans. We will be keeping you overnight and the OB/GYN will see you in the morning to discuss your options. Your room is being prepared now. Hopefully it won't be too much longer before we can get you in a room. Do you have any questions?" I am taking in everything he said. I'm winded.

"Not right now," is all I come up. Then he leaves.

"Sissy, it's getting late. I need to let mom and dad, the kids, and your niece know what's going on with you. I'll be up here after I get off work tomorrow. Love you."

I am afraid, but I don't want Shannon to know. I really want her to stay, heck, she can crawl in bed and stay with me, but I just muster, "Okay, I love you too sissy." When Shannon leaves, I am more alone than I've ever felt before. Finally, after 1:30 a.m., I get a room. Laying in the darkness and stillness of my hospital room, the reality of what the doctor said finally sets in. I replay his diagnosis: "You are the sickest person that we've seen tonight. We are trying to save your life." Oh my, I can't die; I have too much to do. My life is finally falling into place. I am happy, finally happy. Why is this happening to me now, why God, why?

My sleep is interrupted by the nurse asking if I want breakfast, standing over my bed with a tray in hand. Discombobulated, it takes me a moment to adjust. "Sure," I utter. "You are on a liquid diet until the doctor says differently. After you eat, I'll get your meds, okay hun?" A different doctor enters the room with a small team. We exchange pleasantries, but the doctor soon gets to the point: "You're a very sick woman, Allison. I've looked at your charts and you have several fibroid cysts; you're going to have to have a hysterectomy. It will be a laparoscopic partial. We're going to try to save your ovaries. Right now, you're too sick for me to perform the operation. First, we have to get this infection cleared and schedule the surgery afterwards. You'll be here a couple of more days, then you'll see me at my office in a week and we'll schedule the surgery after that."

"What about my uterus, it feels like my uterus is falling out and I'm very swollen, down there." The doctor looks perplexed. I explain why I came to the hospital in the first place. He pulls the covers back and lifts my gown. His eyes bulge as if he's never seen anything like it before. "You are quite swollen. I'll have the nurse give you something for the swelling."

After spending two days in the hospital, I am discharged, and Shannon takes me home. Over the next few days, the swelling in my vagina worsens. The lips of my vagina are so distorted that it looks like fingers twisting into gang signs, or that Mike Tyson has sucker punched me in the crotch. The pain and swelling are unbearable. I can barely walk, so my father takes me back to the ER the Sunday before Labor Day. One of the ER nurses takes a glance and immediately identifies the culprit as a Bartholin cyst that has abscessed. She is empathetic since she too experienced the same. I receive a shot in the vulva to numb the area. Tears run down my face. In agony, the doctor lances and drains the cyst... finally some relief. During my follow-up visit I inform the doctor that I had gone back to the hospital for the swelling and pain. I am cleared to have the surgery, scheduled on September 18th, but I'm not cleared to return to work.

While home, I receive a call from Bonita. After pitching the story, the editor doesn't like the angle of the story and wants Bonita to do a follow-up story, and to have Scott take more pictures. A few days later, they come over and I answer more questions, and Scott takes more photos. Bonita informs me that the story is scheduled to run in the living section of the paper on September 18th, the same day as my surgery.

My parents drive me to the hospital, looking worried as we sit in the waiting before receiving my instructions for the day. Once I am placed in a room, the anesthesiologist introduces himself and explains his role. He is a handsome African American man with milk chocolate skin. "The doctor is running behind schedule today. He had an unscheduled delivery this morning. As soon as he is available, we'll get started." He then exits the room.

My parents and I exchange small talk. Daddy unrolls the newspaper and starts reading. He comes across my article and starts reading some of it out loud. The look of worry is replaced with pride. Daddy hands the article to me when he finishes reading it. "You're famous. Our daughter is famous now," Daddy jokes. Mom giggles. My phone rings. "Hello." "Hi, I just read your article in the newspaper. I wanted to speak with you about some clothes that I acquired through a house I bought. I wanted to see if you might be interested in purchasing some of them for your store.

"Ma'am, I'm in the hospital, getting ready to have surgery, but if you give me your name and number, I'll call you when I get out of the hospital."

"Oh, I'm so sorry. How about I call you back in a couple of weeks?"

"That will be fine."

"Great. Again, I am sorry. I wish you a speedy recovery."

"Thank you." We hang up.

"Who was that?" Daddy asks. "It was someone that read the article and wants to know if I'd be interested in purchasing some clothes for my business. She is going to give me a call back in a few weeks."

"See, I told you that you're famous," Dad nods with approval. We all laugh. The anesthesiologist returns to let us know it was time to head to surgery. My parents and I exchange "I love you's" and I am whisked away.

When I wake up, tubes dangle from my arms and a catheter is attached. I'm drowsy and uncomfortable. A nurse enters the room to take my vitals and check my IV. "Hi, I'm Jan. I'll be your nurse for the evening. How are you feeling?" She doesn't wait for an answer. "You've been in recovery for a few hours. Your parents are still here. They've been faithfully waiting for you to come out of surgery. We're going to let them come in and see you.

"I'm in a lot of pain." The nurse hands a few pain meds to me, along with a cup of water, then steps out of the room. Daddy and Momma come in. "How are you feeling?" they say in unison, both looking tired and worried.

"I'm in pain, but the pain medicine should kick in soon. It's been a long day for you both. Y'all should go home and get some rest."

Dad replies, "We wanted to make sure that you were okay." "I'm, fine. I appreciate you both." They stay for about fifteen more minutes, we hug, exchange another "I love you," and they leave. I lay in silence, staring at the walls. Hospitals creep me out. They are always very cold, and you don't get much rest because by the time you drift off to sleep, nurses interrupt by checking vitals, IV and bringing meds or a meal. In my case, a liquid assortment.

I drift off but am awakened by a tap on the door. Chas walks in. "Hey Allie-oop, I just dropped by after work to check on you." Hey, Chas." I'm not going to stay long, just wanted to lay my eyes on you and see how the surgery went." "

It went well. I'm sore and this catheter is uncomfortable."

"Sorry you're going through this. I'm just glad it's over with, now to recovery." We chat a while longer. Soon after Chas leaves, Shannon brings Timothy to see me. He's so excited that he nearly climbs in bed when he leans in to hug me. "I love you, mom!"

"I love you too, son." They stay for a little while, but I keep dozing off. Timothy wakes me before they leave. I give him a hug and a kiss. "I'll check on you later," Shannon says as they walk out of the room. I drift off to sleep shortly afterwards.

The next morning, the doctor makes his rounds as I was drinking my liquid breakfast. "Good morning," I say.

"Good morning to you. You are one strong lady. I can't believe you are sitting up. I removed three tumors like this." He extends his hands in the form of a small basketball.

"You're really one strong lady. How are you feeling this morning?"

"I'm sore."

"That is expected, especially with the amount of trauma that your body has been through. It will be at least eight to ten weeks before you are healed." He examines me as we continue small talk.

"We'll have you out of here in a couple of days. We'll see how you're doing and make a decision tomorrow. Wow, you are really strong," he repeats. "I'll see you tomorrow. Let the nurses know if you need anything. Have a good day." The next few days are a blur, filled with visitors, sleeping and a lot of medicine.

Road to Recovery

I am scheduled to miss work for the next six weeks. The first few weeks are challenging as I can barely get around and cannot leave the house. KoKoa and I have cabin fever. He is used to being on the go with me, so this being in the house business isn't working for him. When I have to get something out of the car, he jumps in and refuses to get out. Reaching for him, he jumps between the front and back seat or he goes to the opposite side of the car. After a few rounds of this game, I leave him in the car and leave the house door open. I call him. He peeks out the car door but refuses to come in the house. I set the microwave, and when he hears the *ding* he thinks he's getting food and dashes into the house. I laugh so hard, but he doesn't think it's funny. After I close the doors, he stands by the door and pouts for nearly an hour. Poor baby, I know how he feels. I want to go outside too. I have a bright idea to buy a wheelchair off Craigslist. I figure I can convince someone to take me out of the house. That doesn't quite go over well with everyone, but I don't give up. Shannon refuses to push me in the wheelchair, but she takes me to Walmart. I ride in one of the motorized buggies. That is a sight to see. I pass by the feminine products and give a kick and a low shout that I no longer have the need for these products anymore.

I eventually return the call to the lady who called me while I was in pre-op. The house she bought was full of stuff from the previous owner who passed away, and the new owner wants to sell the clothes to me. The clothes are retro and not quite the style for my business, but I do purchase a few pieces for myself and buy a few other items from her. As I get stronger, I resume working on building Closet Chic & Re-Mix Clothing.

Cara is instrumental in helping me during my recovery. She is the wind beneath my wings and I convince her to take me out of the house, minus the wheelchair. We spend countless hours shopping, completing inventory and photographing clothes. Some days we work until the wee hours of the morning. Cara believes in the business and in me, and she supports me in the process. My clients are loyal and patient during my recovery. As I heal and resume selling clothes, they wait to purchase and spread the word. They post pictures of themselves in their clothes, give a testimony about their experience and tag me in the pictures. My clientele is growing, and I am elated!

The doctor extends my time off for an additional two weeks. I return to work in November, a few weeks before the holidays. I am moving and shaking with Closet Chic & Re-Mix Clothing. I am vending, doing fashion shows, personal shopping and making appearances on stage at Sharon's shows. Life is good! I am in my element, doing what I love and helping women look and feel great. The business is a ministry, the clothes lead women to me and conversations and camaraderie emerges. I am back out on the party scene, attending a variety of events. Tulsa has a lot of good parties during the holiday season. I attend most, dressed to the nines and promoting my business.

Men

I attend the Roaring Twenties party at Greenwood Cultural Center and run into Danny, who's here with a date. Ouch! Cara notices him as well. I try to mask that I am bothered, but she sees right through it. "Look at him. I don't like *him*. Look at him with that woman, she's not as classy as you are, sis." Her attempts fail to make me feel better, but they also make me reflect on the events of my life over the past month.

From time to time, Jamal and I talk and catch up. He always tells me how much he still loves me. On the day he found out about my surgery, he told me that he wouldn't know what he'd do if something were to happen to me, and as usual about how much he loves me.

He too is on his way to the ER. I ask him about whether someone will be with him, but no one will be there to be by his side. I am really worried about him and tell him that I'd be devasted if something happens to him.

"Are you dating? Do you have a girlfriend?"

He's silent, then says that he's pulling into the hospital.

"You didn't answer my question, Jamal. Do you have a girlfriend?"

Though we'd been apart for a while, I always thought that eventually we'd get our act together and get married. We have a long history.

"I'm walking in the ER. I'll call you back."

"Really?"

He sighs. "No, I don't have a girlfriend, Allison. I have a wife. I got married. I didn't want to tell you like this, I'm sorry. I've got to go. I'll call you back later." He hangs up.

I am speechless, my heart sinks. Married! How could he? I feel faint. Married, really? I call him back, but he doesn't answer. Damn, that's a blow. That is absolutely the last bit of news that I expected to hear in this lifetime. Tears stream down my face. I feel a deep sorrow, like I'd just lost a family member. The news of Jamal getting married sends me strolling down memory lane and questioning God all over again. *Why God, why? I was supposed to be his wife, why didn't we work out?* I spend the day in a somber mood. The one thing that can change my mood is shopping, so I head out. In the midst of my shopping frenzy, Jamal calls back. Standing between the racks of clothes, I listen to him explain how he wishes that it was me that was walking down the aisle to meet him at the altar. With presumably a straight face, this joker tells me how much he loves me and has never gotten over me, and how he wants us to remain friends. "Friends, are you fucking kidding me? There were plenty of times that we've talked, that you could have mentioned that you'd gotten married. Hell, when we slept together last December you had to be engaged! I'm so fucking done. Wow, Jamal, really? What you are going to do, invite the kids and I to Thanksgiving dinner? Are we gonna hang out? I'm not interested in being your friend. Have a nice life and don't call me back, ever!"

"But I do still love you, I always will Allison."

"I'm hurt!"

"You wouldn't be still, you kept moving and running. I chased you to Arizona the first time. You have no idea how hard it was to leave you there and get on that plane and come back to Georgia. You broke my heart first. I never really got over that. I still love you, but she was here for me when you weren't."

His words are like a slap in the face and a kick to the belly. I feel a huge lump in my throat. I am not ready to confront that truth. I don't tell him I was afraid of him leaving me and that was the reason that I constantly ran. It didn't matter now; it's too late. "I've got to go, Allison, I love you."

"Please don't say that to me, Jamal." We end the call. I am still standing between the racks of clothes frazzled, even the clothes can't soothe these blues. I leave the basket full of clothes in the aisle. In this moment, I am a still a dressed up mess.

Tonight, I'm sitting here watching Danny gallivant across the dance floor with another woman. He notices me and shortly after makes his way over to our table. He speaks to Cara, and she dryly responds. He stands over me and makes small talk. I haven't seen him in months. His deep baritone voice, his cologne and his handsome features are making me weak. Damn, I hate that I have this weakness for men! I quickly make an excuse and leave the table. I head to the ladies' room. On my way back, a gentleman stops me and calls me to his table. He asks my name and to save a dance for him. I tell him that I will. He makes me keep my word by coming to my table to find me. Lucky for me, he's funny, tall, dark and handsome, and he likes to dance. Lawrence keeps my attention off Danny, tonight and many months that follow.

Lawrence is charismatic and handy. He works on cars, houses and has plenty of entertaining stories. Interestingly, he and Danny are the same age. He looks young. His deep chocolate skin and his 6'5" frame is youthful. His thick beard and mustache are dark without the slightest bit of gray. He's a great distraction. As Closet Chic & Re-Mix Clothing grows, he is right here with me, picking up additional racks and equipment, setting up, rearranging, or whatever I need him for. He keeps me laughing. Lawrence recently relocated back to Tulsa after having lived in California for over twenty years. His life is in transition and so is mine. I am doing well in Tulsa, but I still have ambitions to return to Atlanta. We spend a great deal of time together, but as his work schedule gets established our schedules start to conflict. We see one another less and less but speak regularly. We fill a void for one another, and though unspoken, we understand the role in each other's lives. Georgia is in on my mind and I will not be distracted.

Exit Plan

New Year, new beginning, blah, blah, blah. Resolutions are made and quickly broken, but this year I am not making a resolution. "I declare that this year," oh fuck this is hard to say. "Oh, my, okay, this year I declare..." Why do I feel short of breath and my heart palpitates? I feel a nervous energy all over me, my palms sweat and I feel jittery. I take a deep breath and slowly exhale.

"Come on girl, you can do this," I try to convince myself. Okay, I'm tripping, this can't be this hard to say. "I declare that I am no longer a whore to labels and I will not sell my soul for a sale. I can detox from shopping—yes I can!"

Whew, I did it. I said it and I mean it. I've got to stop shopping for me. I am out of space. Every closet in the house is full. I've already carved a small corner in the garage with my personal clothes, intruding on space for Closet Chic and Re-Mix. Clients have ventured to my personal rack and attempt to purchase my clothes. "Sorry, this rack is not for sale."

I can admit, "My shopping is out of control." Wait, I don't think I've ever said that out loud. What's happening to me? Shopping has been an intricate part of me for as long as I can recall; it's what I do, it's who I am. There would be no Closet Chic and Re-Mix Clothing if it weren't for my love of shopping. Shopping has been my drug, the need to shop is my pusher. My identity revolves around my clothes, especially now with the business. Dressing up completes me. What am I doing? Am I making the right decision? This is one of those times in life for a hard truth. I need to save some money so that I can get up out of here. The only way that I'm going to save is if I stop spending, so I must do this cold turkey. I just won't go to the stores. In fact, I won't even drive down the streets that the stores are on. I will avoid shopping at all costs! The first few weeks of my shopping hiatus are brutal, especially with all the after-holiday clearance sales. It doesn't help that I have friends who love to shop and tell me about their great finds. The grand Poohbah of shopping, my mother, calls for me to take her shopping. I can do this, I'm on a mission, I've got to get back to Atlanta.

The first time I walk into my favorite store since my declaration, I am like a kid walking into a candy store. The pressure is on. Walking down the aisle with Mom, I feel the air get thin, my head dizzy.

The colors and prints seem to lift from the fabric, swirl around me and whiff under my nose, as the sweet aroma of a peach cobbler baking in the oven; not just any peach cobbler, my Daddy's peach cobbler, but I resist. Aisle after aisle of clothes call out my name, trying to entice me with their name brands and low prices, which starts to wear on me. Maybe, I'll just try on a few pieces, just to see what I look like in them. No! I am not doing that. I catch a glance of some price tags. This place should be ashamed of themselves trying to pull me in like this. I will not succumb to the pressures of a name brand and great prices. Momma notices that I'm not shopping.

"What's wrong with you?"

"Nothing."

"You're not getting anything?"

"No"

"All these bad clothes and you're not getting anything?"

"No, I'm good."

"Go on and get you a few pieces. I'll buy them for you."

Whew, talk about being under pressure. I see why addicts need to recluse themselves from their addict friends. I feel like a crackhead needing a hit. I almost fall for it, because technically it isn't me spending my money if my mother buys it, right? *God, where are you? You said you'd never leave me or forsake me, but I am starting to doubt You.*

I almost give in but then say, "If you want to give me some money, you can, but I'm saving to move, and I don't need any clothes."

My mother looks as if she sees a ghost. Who am I? Did I just turn down free clothes? I simply cannot go shopping with my mother if I stand a chance at kicking this habit, I mean addiction. I've got to cut my mother off cold turkey, too. I will not survive if I hang out with her. This is the first time that I successfully refuse to shop. Though it hurts, I am glad I did it! There are many times that I desperately want to relapse but the longer I refuse to shop, the easier it gets. Over the next few months, I focus my attention on building my business and saving to move.

"Happy Birthday!" Cara exclaims, as we enjoy a margarita and wait for our food to arrive. El Tequila is one of my favorite spots, good food and even better margaritas. Wow, time flies, another birthday and I'm still in Tulsa. Cara asks what I have planned for the day and wants to take me to dinner, which is all the celebrating I want to do at this point. We agree to dinner, but I tell her that I'm not really in the party mood.

"I'm so ready to get out of here Cara."

"I know girl, I am too. I'm still waiting for the house to sell. As soon as it sells, I'm out!"

"I know that's right!"

"I've got you something."

"Cara, you didn't have to get me anything!"

"I know. Open it!" I empty the gift bag of decorative tissue and find moving starter pack – a journal, magic markers, tape, scissors, and labels. "It's time sis. If you start planning and packing it will seem more real."

"Thanks sis, you're right. Three years in Tulsa is too much. No more. I will be back in Atlanta by July 31st.

Chas outdoes herself tonight. What was supposed to be a quiet dinner for two ends up with an entourage of friends in a stretched SUV limo: sightseeing, club hopping, dancing and drinking. I'll admit she really surprised me. I have some wonderful friends here. Sometimes I wish that I can take my friends and family with me, build a community and live happily ever after, but reality has a way of etching itself back in and unfortunately life doesn't work like that.

I put my moving starter pack to use by writing a to-do list, I break it down with weekly tasks. I add a calendar to the pack so that I can mark off each passing day. I buy moving boxes and Cicely, Timothy and I slowly purge and pack. You never realize how much you accumulate until it's time to move. I decide to put our things in storage and move in with my parents to save more money. Shutting down Closet Chic & Re-Mix Clothing is a tough decision as I have accumulated so much inventory and have a steady clientele, plus shopping for other people satisfies my urge to shop. I personally contact my preferred clients, my A-1's from day one. Some have become girlfriends and others Facebook friends. They've supported me and referred clients to me. It saddens me to inform them that I'm closing shop, but I ensure them that I will resume once I'm settled in Atlanta, and plus I'll offer them fashions from there. I make the announcement on my business and personal pages, and I receive a lot of well wishes and some bittersweet remarks. It feels like an end of an era that I'd just started. Though I often complain about living in Tulsa, some great things have come from it and Closet Chic was certainly one of them.

As I am clean out my closet, I notice a small mountain of weave piled on the floor. I am sure that over the years, I've put a few Asian kids through college or at least spent enough for a large down payment on a house. Gazing at the pile of braided hair, tracks and wigs, made me realize that I've been a slave to weave. Boy, do I have some hair stories. The insecurities I have around my soft dandelion hair keeps me trapped in the maze of weave. It is hard to admit that I am afraid to wear my own hair. I haven't cut or permed it in years. Sometimes it's an analogy for my life – I am afraid to reveal my true self to the world. It seems the more I work on self, the more that I discover that I am a still a mess.

"I'm throwing it all away," I mutter to myself. "Well, maybe not all of it. Let me try these wigs on and see which ones are going to make it to Atlanta. Now Sasha, she's one of my favorites; we've had some good times together, yep, she's going for sure."

I try on wigs for the next half hour, separating those that make the team and those that are being cut. I know I need to embrace my own hair, but not today. I know that I am still a mess, but I am a mess making progress. Eventually I will address all my mess, but right now I'll take the progress.

The closer it gets to moving, the more excited I get! I am ready to start my life in Atlanta again! I pack a little each day after work and nearly all day long on the weekends. We're almost out of here! I can hardly believe it's been almost three years. I convince the kids and myself that we can tolerate moving in with their grandparents. I know that I will have to pack my patience but it's necessary. For now, I've got to get the rest of this packing done so that we can move our things to storage. I know what will get me through this. Let me pop in some Mary J. and pour me a glass a wine. "Let's get it percolating while we're waiting in this dancery." I dance through the house, getting a workout. I sip on wine and listen to Mary pour her heart out. While Mary sings, I sip and pack. "Share my world, don't you leave, promise I'll be here whenever you need me. If you look at my life and see what I've seen." I pack and sip some more. I reminisce over my life, especially these last few years. I swear she has a song for all of life's situations.

"Real Love, that's my ish." I turn the volume up full blast. "Now how many times I have thought I had a real love. I thought you were the answer to the questions in my mind, but it seems that I was wrong, but if I stay strong maybe I'd find my real love...." I belt the verses out with Mary. I thought Jamal was the answer, hell, Austin's crazy ass and Danny too!

"See I'm searching for a real love and I don't where to go. Been around the world and high and low and still I never know. How it feels to have a real love 'cause it seems it's not around. Gotta end it in this way 'cause it seems he can't be found." I feel you Mary. I thought I found him in Mitchell, Lawrence and many others. Damn, I've got to look at my life and get it together. All these damn men and I'm still alone. They don't measure up. One of us always leaves; it just never works out. The only man that has never let me down or walked out my life is my Daddy. They don't make them like him anymore. Daddy is a special and rare breed. I can count on him like clockwork, he's always been here for me. He's been a father figure for Cicely and Timothy. He takes care of the home; my mother has never had to work. Daddy looks out for everyone, sometimes to a fault... he'd give his last dime. My Daddy is my hero. Where are the men like Daddy? I guess I'll always be a Daddy's girl.

I turn the music off. Mary has my emotions all over the place right now. At least I finish packing. My cell phone rings.

"Hello."

"Where have you been? I've been calling you for almost an hour."

Daddy sounds worried.

"I've been packing, and the music was playing. I didn't hear the phone ring. Is everything okay?"

"I guess, it will be."

"What do you mean by that?"

"I went to the doctor today and they said I have cancer."

"CANCER, what do you mean?" The room spins. I feel faint. "What kind? What stage is it in? What type of treatments will you have to have?" I feel a lump in my throat and my stomach is queasy. I feel like I am about to throw up.

"Daddy, let me call you back." I hang up and sit in silence. Cancer, FUUUUCCCCCCK, I'm stuck!!!!!!!!! The room feels as if it is closing in on me. The boxes and clothes mesh together. I am nauseated. I need a drink of water, but I don't have the energy to make it to the kitchen. My dad is my hero, I can't lose him, but I can't stay here either. A sharp pain shoots through my head. I grab the wall for support. I can't breathe. I slide down the wall curl up into a ball and sob. I don't know what to do. This is a decision I am not ready to make.

Made in the USA
Monee, IL
18 June 2021